Writing and Communication Masters

Language Network

D1537782

McDougal Littell

A HOUGHTON MIFFLIN COMPANY

Evanston, Illinois   •   Boston   •   Dallas

ISBN 0-618-05315-8

Copyright © 2001 by McDougal Littell Inc.
All rights reserved. Printed in the United States of America.

Permission is hereby granted to teachers to reprint or photocopy in classroom quantities the pages or
sheets in this work that carry a McDougal Littell copyright notice. These pages are designed to be
reproduced by teachers for use in their classes with accompanying McDougal Littell material, provided each
copy made shows the copyright notice. Such copies may not be sold, and further distribution is expressly
prohibited. Except as authorized above, prior written permission must be obtained from McDougal Littell
Inc. to reproduce or transmit this work or portions thereof in any other form or by any other electronic or
mechanical means, including any information storage or retrieval system, unless expressly permitted by
federal copyright law. Address inquiries to Manager, Rights and Permissions, McDougal Littell Inc., P.O.
Box 1667, Evanston, IL 60204.

1 2 3 4 5 6 7 8 9 – CKI – 04 03 02 01 00

Contents

Writing Workshops

22 Proposal

23 Dramatic Scene

24 Research Report

Communicating in the Information Age

25 Using Information Resources

26 Evaluating Ideas

Special Features

Use *Writing and Communication Masters* to reinforce skills taught in the Essential Writing Skills, Writing Workshops, and Communicating in the Information Age chapters of the Pupil's Edition.

Name _____ Date _____

Worksheets correspond to lessons in the Pupil's Edition.

Lesson 4

Combining with Phrases and Appositives

Instruction focuses on a topic or skill and is followed by reinforcement activities. Keywords and phrases are highlighted for greater clarity and ease of use.

An appositive identifies or explains a noun or pronoun. If you have two sentences that offer information about the same noun or pronoun, you can combine them by changing one of the sentences into an appositive.

Two sentences can often be combined by moving a group of words from one sentence to the other.

> **Jo and Kim take a vacation every year. They vacation *in the mountains*.**
> **Jo and Kim take a vacation *in the mountains* every year.**

Sometimes you must change the ending of one of the words to *-ing* or *-ed*.

> **We saw a horse. The horse *galloped across the field*.**
> **We saw a horse *galloping across the field*.**

At other times, you will have to separate the added group of words with commas.

> **Andrea Welden spoke at the meeting. Andrea Welden is *an astronomer*.**
> **Andrea Welden, *an astronomer*, spoke at the meeting.**

Adding Groups of Words

Join each sentence pair to eliminate any repeated or unnecessary words. These words have been italicized. Use only the three combination techniques above.

1. The folk singer performs tonight. ***He will perform*** at Krytes Stadium.

   _____

2. Althea's optometrist measured her eyes for contact lenses. ***The optometrist*** used special equipment. (Use a comma.)

   _____

3. Glenda turned on the radio. ***The radio was*** in her room.

   _____

4. That woman is Dr. Janet Mahoney. ***Dr. Mahoney is*** the new superintendent. (Use a comma.)

   _____

5. Eric heard the wind. ***The wind*** howled outside.

   _____

6. In the attic we found some clothing. ***The clothing was*** from the 1930s.

   _____

7. Robert Duvall starred in the movie. ***Robert Duvall*** is an Academy Award winner. (Use a pair of commas.)

   _____

8. The sunflowers are immense! ***The sunflowers*** grow at the edge of the garden.

   _____

Tabs make it easy to navigate the book.

Each page clearly refers to its corresponding part in the Pupil's Edition for easy reference.

CHAPTER 16

Copyright © McDougal Littell Inc.

For use with Pupil's Edition pp. 372–373

Lesson 1 Limiting a Topic

The scope of the topic for a specific writing situation is determined by your purpose, audience, and form. When the topic you have been assigned or have chosen is too general, you can use one of the following techniques to focus it: **questioning, browsing, graphic devices, freewriting, listing,** and **brainstorming.**

Using a Focusing Technique

For each of the general topics below, use the technique indicated in parentheses to focus and limit it. Write your new limited topic on the line provided.

1. Topic: Freedom of Speech (Write questions to help you limit your topic.)

_____

_____

_____

_____

_____

Focused Topic: _____

2. Topic: Explorers in Canada (Browse through reference books to help you focus your topic.)

_____

_____

_____

_____

_____

Focused Topic: _____

3. Topic: The Internet (Freewrite to discover what ideas and details you already know.)

_____

_____

_____

_____

_____

Focused Topic: _____

Lesson 3

Sharing Your Writing

Think about how to share your revised writing. Here are some options.

Self-Publishing
Zines
Writing groups or workshops

Formal Publishing
School or local newspaper
Literary magazine
Student anthologies
Yearbook
Local or national writing
  contests
Trade magazines

Electronic Forums
Create your own Web site
Online magazine
Online school newspaper
Online bulletin boards
E-mail

Live Forums
Talent shows
Drama clubs
In-class presentations
Open-mike night

Choosing Among Publishing Options

For each writing idea, choose a publishing option and explain why you chose it.

1. A skit about a historical figure _____

_____

2. A letter protesting the closing of the library on Saturdays _____

_____

3. An essay on the role of oil in today's economy _____

_____

4. A song for a school musical _____

_____

5. An article about a local woman's 100th birthday party _____

_____

6. A poem about the death of a pet _____

_____

7. An advertisement for home-baked goods _____

_____

8. An article on the school volleyball team _____

_____

9. A science fiction story _____

_____

10. A letter supporting the right of students to protest _____

For use with Pupil's Edition pp. 295–297

Lesson 2

Writing Introductions

Your introduction is one of the most important parts of your composition. It sets the tone of your composition, captures your reader's attention, and states your thesis. You can use your introduction to engage interest in one of several ways.

Make a surprising statement
Address readers directly
Begin with a quotation
Pose a question
Draw an analogy

Writing Effective Introductions

For each topic that follows, use the method suggested in parentheses to develop a short, effective introduction to a composition.

1. The worst storm you've seen (Present a description.) _____

   _____

   _____

   _____

   _____

2. The problem of students cutting classes (Make a surprise statement.) _____

   _____

   _____

   _____

   _____

3. The positive effects of aerobic exercise (Pose a question.) _____

   _____

   _____

   _____

   _____

Lesson 2

Writing Conclusions

When you conclude a piece of nonfiction writing, be sure to give your readers a sense of resolution. Your conclusion should tie together the important information in your composition and leave your reader with a lasting impression. You can conclude a composition in a number of ways.

Restate the thesis
Summarize
Generalize
Make a prediction
Call readers to action

Writing a Conclusion

Read this portion of an essay. Write two different conclusions for it, using two of the methods described above.

> Each year, violent crime in the New York City subways rises and ridership falls. Statistics confirm this; city leaders discuss it; concerned citizens call for change; yet the situation continues to worsen. After each of the more shocking incidents, the number of transit officers on each train increases, but transit officers cost money, and the city will not allocate more money.
>
> As people stay away from the subway in droves, the Transit Authority faces a larger and larger budget deficit. If the authority's answer is to save money by cutting service, riders will continue to drop out because of train delays and other inconveniences. If the authority's answer is to raise fares, riders will still leave because the service is not worth the price.

1. _____

_____

_____

_____

_____

_____

2. _____

_____

_____

_____

_____

_____

For use with Pupil's Edition p. 306

Methods of Organization

Lesson 3

Compositions need to be organized. In most cases, your audience and purpose determine your organization. Other times, you will have to determine how the ideas and facts of a given topic are related. The following are some ways to organize details.

Comparison-and-Contrast Order similarities and differences, subject by subject or point by point

Cause-and-Effect Order points out why something occurred

Problem-Solution identifies a problem and then explains how it might be solved

Inductive Organization leads readers to a general conclusion by citing specific examples

Deductive Organization supports a general statement with specific examples

Classification relates characteristics

Degree describes relationships by degree of importance, familiarity, or complexity

Chronological order presents events in order

Spatial Order describes in terms of spatial organization

Organizing Ideas

Read the following lists of information gathered for writing projects on different topics. While you are reading, think about the different methods for organizing information. Then decide which method of organization you would use for each list, and write the letters of the sentences in the order in which you would arrange the information.

1. Beach Scene

   A. Bright towels topped with sunbathers formed a vibrant patchwork on the sand.

   B. A hundred yards out, a windsurfer rose and fell with the waves.

   C. We stood on a high dune and surveyed the beach below us.

   D. A dozen other people jumped or rode the shiny green waves.

   E. A large tanker steamed slowly across the horizon.

2. Wildlife Conservation

   A. Scientists have learned much about medicine, pollution, and various life processes by studying wildlife.

   B. All wildlife is important in helping to maintain the earth's ecosystem and thus ensuring our continued survival.

   C. Wild species of animals and plants are economic resources, providing food and materials for many nations.

   D. We should work to preserve wild animals and plants because they contribute to the beauty of nature.

Lesson 4

Achieving Coherence

When your ideas flow structurally and logically, you have achieved coherence in your writing. There are three main techniques to help you organize your writing coherently.

Links between paragraphs repeated words and transitional phrases link paragraphs

Transitional paragraphs an entire paragraph can be used as a transition in longer pieces of writing

Word chains key words, synonyms, and related ideas repeated from sentence to sentence

A. Identifying Word Chains

Read these paragraphs. Underline the words used in the word chains in each paragraph.

1. Kyra had never wanted something the way she wanted that horse. She dreamed about it. The animal occupied all of her waking hours. She was obsessed by it.

2. The war was everywhere. Television news announced war. Sitcoms joked about war. Shopkeepers chatted war, and students debated war. Even little children knew all about the war; it was the most important topic in daily life.

B. Using Transitional Devices

Read these paragraphs. Revise them, including at least two transitional devices. Write your revised paragraphs on a separate sheet of paper.

Almost everyone is familiar with the body of literature known as the Arthurian legends. Not surprisingly, these legends are not the original tales first told in the Middle Ages. They have been influenced by many writers and have changed so much that we don't know what is fact and what is fiction. The legends themselves are contradictory too.

Legends say that Arthur was born illegitimately of Uther Pendragon, a Welsh noble, and Igrayne, the wife of the duke of Gorlois. Merlin supposedly took the infant to live with a lord named Ector but did not reveal the boy's royal heritage. Thirteen years later, after Uther died, Arthur performed the deed that was to designate the new king, pulling the sword Excalibur out of a stone.

Arthur was probably nothing more than a great leader of some Celtic tribe. The earliest reference to Arthur can be found in the poem *Gododdin* from the seventh century A.D. The Welsh historian Nennius told some of the first Arthurian tales in his *History of the Britons* and in the appendix to it, titled *Mirabilia*, or "Marvels."

For use with Pupil's Edition pp. 312–313

Lesson 1

How to Elaborate

When you elaborate, you add details to enhance your message, providing the reader with more and better information. You can elaborate for different reasons and using different methods.

Sensory details make descriptions concrete and believable.

Similes and metaphors convey specific qualities and feelings.

Anecdotes, definitions, analogies, and **examples** clarify meaning or explain your point.

Facts, statistics, reasons, and **expert testimony** support opinions and arguments.

Images, diagrams, charts, and **graphs** clarify or enhance information visually.

Adding Details for Elaboration

1. Rewrite the description below using sensory details.

> The room was very quiet. Jaime could hear the clock as he looked over the test. He was so nervous that he could barely read the instructions.

_____

_____

_____

_____

_____

_____

2. Rewrite the essay below, adding examples, incidents, or opinions.

> When the 1980s ended, people returned to the comfortable, safe things in life. Home-cooked food, soft, inviting furniture, well-built cars, comfortable clothing—all point to a need for reassurance, a fear of the unfamiliar, and a desire to return to the past.

_____

_____

_____

_____

_____

_____

CHAPTER 13

Lesson 3

Quotations

Quotations can lend authority or summarize a point. A quote can be useful in research papers or other forms of writing, but only if it helps the writer clarify the message or significantly reinforce or add meaning to it.

Using and Documenting Quotations

Write two paragraphs that incorporate the quotes below. Remember, the quote should help elaborate your main point.

1. "Happy families are all alike; every unhappy family is unhappy in its own way."

—Leo Tolstoy, *Anna Karenina*

_____

_____

_____

_____

_____

_____

_____

_____

2. "I like the trees because they seem more resigned to the way they have to live than other things do."

—Willa Cather, *O Pioneers!*

_____

_____

_____

_____

_____

_____

_____

_____

For use with Pupil's Edition pp. 324–326

CHAPTER 13

Thesis Statements

A **thesis statement** is the most important element of your composition. It states your purpose, the main idea, and your position on that idea, and it focuses your composition. Each paragraph in a composition should develop and support your thesis statement. A thesis statement should be specific, arguable, and interesting.

A. Writing Thesis Statements

For each numbered item below, write a thesis statement that reveals the main idea to be developed in a short essay. Each of the sentences provided is a topic sentence for a paragraph in the essay.

1. Thesis statement: _____

_____

- Modern zoos have replaced cages with habitats, where animals live in spaces that are more open and designed to resemble their native environments.
- Many of today's zoos have captive breeding programs to help save endangered species and educational programs to involve citizens in the effort to save the environment and its wildlife.
- Zoos also conduct research in zoology and biology.

2. Thesis statement: _____

_____

- Today, people watch specific television programs for specific purposes.
- Unlike watching a Broadway play or a movie in a theater, watching television with others provides opportunities for socializing.
- While television is all too often misused as a baby sitter, some programs are educational and teach children important skills.

B. Writing a Thesis Statement

Imagine that the following paragraph is the beginning of a composition. Write a thesis statement that could be developed in the composition.

Thesis statement: _____

_____

    Computer printers and printing presses produce most of the written materials people read. However, handwriting enables both children and adults to informally communicate their ideas to others. In fact, very young children show they are interested in written communication when they scribble on paper; they often can print readable words by the time they reach first grade.

Lesson 2

Revising for Unity and Coherence

When revising your writing, ask yourself the following questions to help you evaluate your work.

Does my draft have a clear focus?
Have I kept the needs of my audience in mind?
Are there enough supporting details?
Are my paragraphs presented in a logical order?
Does each paragraph support the main idea?
Does my writing flow smoothly?

The answers will help you make changes that improve your draft's content and structure. Writers can also ask peer readers to help them identify strengths and weaknesses in their work.

Editing a Draft

Imagine that you have written the following draft of a paper on Shakespeare's *Henry IV, Part I.* Read the draft, concentrating on ideas and form. Then revise it by answering the questions that follow.

> Falstaff is the central comic figure in *Henry IV, Part I.* He is regarded by his fellows as a thief, a liar, a swindler, and a coward. Falstaff the liar exaggerates the Gadshill robbery incident, saying that two, then four, then seven, then nine, then eleven men attacked him. Falstaff is also fat and old. He feels betrayed by his old friend Henry. Cowardly Falstaff runs from a fight. Falstaff the swindler shows his deceitful or fraudulent nature when he has his companions in the Gadshill event bloody their own noses and clothing and then claim that the blood is that of their attackers. Falstaff the liar claims he killed Hotspur in battle.

1. What is the focus of the draft? _____

_____

2. Which supporting details do not relate directly to the focus of the draft? _____

_____

3. Are the details in the draft in a logical order? If not, how could the order be changed

to achieve coherence? _____

_____

_____

4. What points in the paragraph does the audience need to know more about?_____

_____

_____

_____

For use with Pupil's Edition pp. 338–340

CHAPTER 14

Varying Sentence Structure

You can revise dull, repetitious writing by varying the structure, length, and form of your sentences. There are four basic types of sentences.

Simple sentences have one independent clause but no subordinate clauses. They can be varied by using a compound predicate or a participial phrase or by adding subordinate or independent clauses.

> EXAMPLE Joe and Molly moved to Seattle.

Compound sentences have two or more independent clauses.

> EXAMPLE The truck was delayed, and they had to move in without furniture.

Complex sentences have one independent clause and one or more subordinate clauses.

> EXAMPLE When the truck made a stop in Idaho, their furniture was unloaded.

Compound-complex sentences have two or more independent clauses and one or more subordinate clauses.

> EXAMPLE The Idaho family who received the furniture was surprised, and Joe and Molly spent days on the telephone tracking down the truck.

Varying Sentence Structure

Rewrite each group of simple sentences as one sentence, following the directions given in parentheses.

1. An Egyptian pharaoh was entombed with earthly belongings. He expected to continue his mortal life. (simple sentence with participial phrase)_____

_____

2. Radio City Music Hall seats 6,200 people. It is the world's biggest movie theater. The Rockettes perform there. (compound-complex sentence) _____

_____

3. Wendy wanted to become an engineer. Wendy applied to the engineering program at Cornell University. She was accepted there. (complex sentence)_____

_____

4. Acoma, New Mexico, was settled in 1075. It is the oldest continuously inhabited U.S. town. (simple sentence with compound predicate) _____

_____

5. Edgar Allan Poe attended West Point. He was dismissed for misbehavior. (compound sentence) _____

_____

Problem Language

Avoid these types of language when writing.

Clichés are expressions that have lost their impact through overuse. Delete them or refresh them using precise words.

Jargon is technological language that can confuse a reader. Substitute plain English to clarify your meaning.

Gender-Specific Language is offensive to many readers, and it can often be inaccurate. Replace gender-specific words, such as *mailman, man-made,* and *forefathers,* with gender-neutral words, such as *mail carrier, artificial,* and *ancestors.*

Identifying Varieties of Language

Read the examples below. Identify the problem language used in each and then rewrite each sentence, replacing the problem language.

1. The chairman of the board will be the keynote speaker at the luncheon. _____

_____

2. The lake bottom was as dry as a bone, and the air was as hot as Hades. _____

_____

3. The mailman delivered a new script to the actress's dressing room. _____

_____

4. Quiet as a mouse, she crept through the dark hallway._____

_____

CHAPTER 14

For use with Pupil's Edition p. 347

Proofreading

Proofreading, or revising for grammar and punctuation, is the final step of the revising process. During this stage, you read your draft over carefully to find and correct errors in grammar, usage, punctuation, capitalization, and spelling. Your goal in proofreading is to create an error-free final draft that could be submitted for publication. The following symbols will help you when you proofread.

Proofreading Marks			
∧	insert letters or words	◡	close up
⊙	insert a period	¶	begin a new paragraph
∧	insert a comma	≡	capitalize a letter
#	add a space	/	make a capital letter lower case
ℐ	delete letters or words	∽	transpose the positions of letters or words

Proofreading a Draft

Read the following draft of a short story entitled "Subway." Proofread it for mechanical and grammatical errors. Write your revisions above the text, using the proofreading marks and changing words as necessary.

Reggie looked quickly over his sholder as he decsended the stairs to the subway station. Behind him the street was dark and empty ahead of him the platform was also empty. A testament to the late hour. Reggie suspected that the next train would be the last one of the night. He peared down the tracks and willed it to come. he didn't like riding the subway, he especial didn't like riding it alone late at night. Five minutes later there was a low rumble, a rush of air, and finally the train emerged out of the tunnel. Regie sat on the long bench in the first car staring at the ads above the windows. Then he noticed the other passenger. A heavyset young man in jeans and a T-shirt. The man wore a two-day stubble sunglasses, and a smirk. He looked at Reggie from the far end of the car, Reggie looked away. At the first stop Reggie could see other people on the platform but no one entered his car. At the second stop another young man in jeans and T-shirt gets on. He looked around. "Mike," he said to the other passenger. "Hey, said Mike, 'How're ya doin'?" The newcomer slouched into the seat next to Mike. The two looked at Reggie and then at each other. Reggie knew they were planning some thing.

Formal and Informal Diction

When you write, you must choose whether to express yourself in formal English or informal English. **Formal English** has a serious tone and is typically found in scholarly journals, business communication, speeches, lectures, and textbooks. **Informal English** is more relaxed, though it still follows the rules of good grammar and usage. Informal English is used in conversation, personal letters, and some journalism.

A. Identifying Varieties of English

Read the paragraphs below. Identify the language of each as formal English or informal English.

1. As the economy slows still further, the government has decided to raise prices of basic goods by 60 percent. Leaders assure the people that wage raises and benefits will offset most of the increase, and they have agreed not to raise prices of medical care or fuel.

   _____

2. The island of Saba is an oasis of calm, beauty, and low prices in the Caribbean. I hesitate to tell you about it—it's a secret all those in the know want to keep!— but its special qualities shouldn't be hidden. From the crazy flight in the short-takeoff, short-landing plane to the equally hair-raising taxi ride straight down the mountain at the end of your stay, you'll know you've been somewhere different— exotic—even a little dangerous.

   _____

B. Using Varieties of English

Choose one of the paragraphs above and rewrite it in the opposite variety of English. If it is in formal English, rewrite it in informal English, and vice versa.

_____

_____

_____

_____

_____

_____

_____

_____

For use with Pupil's Edition pp. 354–356

Imagery

Several **poetic devices** can help you communicate a mood. One such device is **imagery,** a word picture you paint by using descriptions of sights, sounds, smells, touches, and tastes. Imagery allows you to show your reader something rather than just tell about it. Notice the difference between telling and showing in the following example.

> The jester tried desperately to please the king.

> Scrambling about on the filthy floor, the jester flung himself from joke to joke. His high-pitched, desperate voice echoed in the hall, but the king ignored him, focusing in the flickering candlelight on the monk seated to his right.

Using Imagery

After you read each of the following sentences, write a short paragraph using imagery that appeals to the senses.

1. The Vienna New Year's Ball was the grandest, most lavish celebration in all Europe.

_____

_____

_____

_____

_____

_____

_____

_____

2. The huge black cloud moved into the valley with almost no warning. _____

_____

_____

_____

_____

_____

_____

_____

_____

CHAPTER 15

Lesson 2

Figurative Language

You can use language in creative ways to make a powerful impact with your writing. One method is to use **figurative language,** or language that goes beyond the literal meanings of the words and makes your reader think about something in a new way. Types of figurative language include

Simile a comparison that uses *like* or *as*

Metaphor an implied comparison

Personification attributing human characteristics to animals or inanimate objects

Hyperbole exaggerating for dramatic effect

Understatement the opposite of hyperbole, often used for comic effect

A. Identifying Figurative Language

Identify the type of figurative language used in each example below.

1. The flames reached out with greedy fingers. _____

2. Tom never made a move without his rabbit's foot. _____

3. The hail sounded like a giant's Ping-Pong game on the roof. _____

4. "Well," Rog sighed, looking over the earthquake's damage, "I did need a new set

of dishes." _____

5. The colors in his shirt clashed like untuned orchestra instruments. _____

6. The roller coaster dipped so suddenly that Marie was sure her vital organs were still

hanging in the air behind her. _____

B. Using Figurative Language

Rewrite each sentence below, using figurative language as indicated in parentheses.

1. The coal miner's face was dirty. (simile) _____

_____

2. Rats followed the Piper as he moved through town. (personification) _____

_____

3. The field of sunflowers was incredibly bright. (hyperbole) _____

_____

4. Lava poured out of the fissure. (metaphor) _____

_____

For use with Pupil's Edition pp. 357–360

CHAPTER 15

Creating Tone

The **tone** of a passage reveals the writer's attitude toward his or her subject. Depending on the language you use, your tone can be any one of the following:

authoritative	humorous	angry
ironic	silly	romantic
sugary	breezy	

You can establish tone in your writing by selecting your words carefully and by altering the complexity of your sentence structures.

Analyzing Tone

Read each of the following passages. Focus on the choice of words and the structure of the sentences. On the lines after each passage, identify the tone of the passage and list the words and phrases that create that tone.

1. Most people who bother with the matter at all would admit that the English language is in a bad way. . . . Our civilization is decadent and our language—so the argument runs—must inevitably share in the general collapse.

   George Orwell, "Politics and the English Language"

   _____

   _____

2. . . . the little girls rushed away in a body, deeply, deeply excited, wild with joy. Some one found a long rope, and they began skipping. And never did they skip so high, run in and out so fast, or do such daring things as on that morning.

   Katherine Mansfield, "The Doll's House"

   _____

   _____

3. . . . she felt herself stiffen slowly into the breathlessness of attention: . . . those two women, and their children, and the man on the train, and the bright and radiant uncurtained room, an island in the surrounding darkness, were symbols to her of things too vague to name, of happiness, of hope, of brightness, warmth, and celebration.

   Margaret Drabble, "A Voyage to Cythera"

   _____

   _____

4. Thirty-five is a very attractive age. London society is full of women of the very highest birth who have, of their own free choice, remained thirty-five for years. Lady Dumbleton is an instance in point. To my own knowledge she has been thirty-five ever since she arrived at the age of forty, which was many years ago now.

   Oscar Wilde, *The Importance of Being Earnest*

   _____

   _____

Lesson 4

Point of View in Nonfiction

The position from which the narrator addresses the audience and views events and characters being described is the **point of view.** You can write nonfiction from three distinct points of view:

First person narrator refers directly to his or her own experiences and ideas and uses first-person pronouns, such as "I," "me," "we," and "us"

Second person narrator refers to the reader as "you"

Third person narrator does not participate in the action, but describes it as happening to others, referring to characters as "he," "she," or "it"

Identifying Point of View in Nonfiction

Read the paragraphs below. Identify the point of view in each.

1. When it comes to French fried potatoes, you have to "do as the Romans do," whether you're in Italy, France, or another European country. In England, for instance, you eat them wrapped in greasy paper and doused with vinegar. You progress to cardboard cones in Belgium, but you must cover the fatty treats in even fattier mayonnaise.

_____

2. Although the giant octopus is a strange-looking beast, I found it to be much gentler and more curious than I expected. The one I followed around the ocean floor quickly decided it would rather follow me, and we engaged in an unusual game of follow-the-leader.

_____

3. The settlers who moved west along the Santa Fe trail, between Missouri and what is now New Mexico, had to face a variety of hardships. These included blizzards in fall, fires in summer, and disease and Indian attacks in all seasons.

_____

4. Professor Micklen guided me out to the site. It was remarkable to see the entire backbone and rib cage of a Tyrannosaurus rex intact, poking up through the arid soil. I was speechless.

_____

CHAPTER 15

For use with Pupil's Edition pp. 363–364

Lesson 5

Understanding Voice

In writing, your voice allows your reader to "hear" a human personality. Each writer's voice is unique, and it is determined by the elements of style—sentence structure, diction, imagery, mechanics, and tone. There are a number of ways that you can discover your voice and reveal it in your writing:

Write for yourself. Without an audience, you are less tempted to try to impress others.

Read you work aloud. Listen for writing that sounds phony or awkward.

Imitate writing you admire. Integrate elements of your favorite writing into your own.

Keep at it. Practice writing. A writer's voice evolves over time.

Finding a Voice

Read the passages below. Then choose a topic of your own and write a passage about it in a style similar to that of one of the pieces.

> People above a certain age should not be allowed to have two cars unless they are identical because these people often have trouble remembering which car they happen to have brought with them. There are few moments in life more damaging to your self-esteem than to leave a football game, a supermarket, or a mall and forget not only where you left your car but where you left your mind because you cannot remember which car it was.
>
> Bill Cosby, *Time Flies*

> "Assertiveness," "Looking out for number one," and other systems for the dissemination of rudeness are abhorrent to Miss Manners. That people should spend hours studying vile little books and then disciplining themselves so as best to add to the general unpleasantness in the world is shocking.
> Why, they could be spending that time learning to behave like Miss Manners.
> Judith Martin, *Miss Manners' Guide to Excruciatingly Correct Behavior*

_____

_____

_____

_____

_____

_____

_____

_____

_____

CHAPTER 15

Stylistic Repetition

One way to develop your writing style is to use various methods to achieve emphasis, or the special attention given to words and phrases to make them stand out. Common techniques include repetition and parallelism.

Repetition repeats important words or phrases.

> It was *the only place* there was. It was the *only way* we could be together, *the only way* I could hold a job.
>
> Tillie Olsen, "I Stand Here Ironing"

Parallelism expresses related concepts in similar forms.

> I saw on that ivory face the expression *of sombre pride, of ruthless power, of craven terror—of an intense and hopeless despair.*
>
> Joseph Conrad, *The Heart of Darkness*

Recognizing Methods of Achieving Emphasis

Read the following passages, and think about the methods of emphasis that are used. Then answer the questions below.

> **(1)** The chief feature of the landscape, and of your life in it, was the air. **(2)** Looking back on a sojourn in the African highlands, you are struck by your feeling of having lived for a time up in the air. **(3)** The sky was rarely more than pale blue or violet, with a profusion of mighty, weightless, ever-changing clouds towering up and sailing on it, but it has a blue vigour in it, and at a short distance it painted the ranges of hills and the woods a fresh deep blue. **(4)** In the middle of the day the air was alive over the land. . . .
>
> Isak Dinesen, *Out of Africa*

1. Which important word from sentence 1 is repeated for emphasis throughout the

   passage? _____

2. Which sentence describes the colors of the landscape? _____

3. Which method of emphasis is used in that sentence? _____

> **(1)** Roaring defiance, Grendel burst into the mead-hall. **(2)** Hideous was his voice; fearful was his countenance. **(3)** Beowulf did not pause, but lunged at the monster, calling on all his strength and cunning; and, massive though he was, the monster faltered. **(4)** That moment's hesitation sealed his doom. **(5)** Now the advantage was Beowulf's; his strength and cunning stood him in good stead. **(6)** Before the stars had paled, Grendel had fled, mortally wounded, into the forest.
>
> Edwin Morgan, translator, *Beowulf*

4. Which sentence describes Grendel's appearance? _____

5. Which methods of emphasis are used in that sentence? _____

6. In sentences 3 and 5, which important words are repeated? _____

For use with Pupil's Edition pp. 371–373

Inverted Sentences

To give your writing a literary or elevated tone, you can invert the subject and verb or move whole phrases to the beginning of a sentence.

Sentence The mail carrier belatedly delivered the express letter at four o'clock.

Revision 1 Belatedly, the mail carrier delivered the express letter at four o'clock. (adverb modifier)

Revision 2 At four o'clock the mail carrier belatedly delivered the express letter. (prepositional phrase)

Revision 3 When it was four o'clock, the mail carrier belatedly delivered the express letter. (subordinate clause)

Varying Sentence Beginnings

Rewrite the sentences below, beginning each sentence as instructed in parentheses.

1. About ten million people worldwide celebrate their birthdays each day. (adverb modifier)__

_____

2. One-third of all U.S. citizens lived on farms during the 1930s. (prepositional phrase)

_____

3. The dig became exciting after we found the first few fossils. (adverbial clause) _____

_____

4. The Venus flytrap emits a sweet smell to attract insects. (infinitive phrase) _____

_____

5. Scientists have studied the language of whales for many years. (prepositional phrase)

_____

6. Children legally had to salute the flag until the law changed in the 1940s. (adverbial clause)

_____

7. Jack-o'-lanterns were made of turnips before they were made of pumpkins. (adverbial clause)

_____

8. We ran across the puddles of water, laughing and splashing. (participial phrase)_____

_____

Varying Sentence Length

You can prevent a monotonous rhythm by varying the length of your sentences. To avoid an awkward succession of short sentences, you may combine them using a single-word modifier, a prepositional phrase, a participial phrase, an appositive, a compound sentence, a simple sentence with a compound predicate, or a subordinate clause.

Separate Sentences Some writers work at home. They conduct much of their business by telephone.

Sentences Combined Some writers work at home and conduct much of their business by telephone. (compound predicate)

Separate Sentences On the second day we spotted an eland. An eland is a type of antelope.

Sentences Combined On the second day we spotted an eland, which is a type of antelope. (subordinate clause)

Varying Sentence Length

Combine each pair of sentences into one effective sentence.

1. Norman Albert set a record for treading water. He didn't stop for 64 hours.

   _____

2. The crew worked day and night. They finished the renovations in a week.

   _____

3. The ospreys spend the summer in Scotland. They migrate to Africa in winter.

   _____

4. She was inside the deep, dark cave. She lit a match.

   _____

5. Vincent van Gogh completed more than 800 oil paintings in his lifetime. Vincent van Gogh sold only one oil painting in his lifetime.

   _____

6. The referee was looking the other way. He missed the foul.

   _____

7. The Masai are herdsmen. Their cattle are their most prized possessions.

   _____

8. Elliot is a talented pianist. Elliot won the music competition.

   _____

CHAPTER 16

For use with Pupil's Edition pp. 376–377

Sound Devices

Sound devices play a key role in poetry, and they can also play an important role in prose writing. Sound devices help create emphasis and intonation. The following are examples of sound devices.

Rhyme repetition of syllables with the same consonant and vowel sounds.

Onomatopoeia words whose sound suggests their meaning

Alliteration repetition of initial consonant sounds

Assonance repetition of an internal vowel sound

Consonance repetition of an internal consonant sound

A. Identifying Sound Devices

Identify the sound device or devices used in each example below.

1. The diver entered the water with hardly a splash. _____

2. The falcon fights free of its jesses and flies toward the sun. _____

3. Before him on the forest floor/Lay Soren, snoring gently. _____

4. Then every evil filled the room and hovered, like a fever cloud. _____

B. Using Sound Devices

Rewrite each sentence below, using the sound device indicated in parentheses.

1. The breeze moved the forest leaves gently. (onomatopoeia) _____

_____

2. The icy tops of the trees glinted in the sunlight. (assonance)_____

_____

3. The boxers circled each other, waiting for the opportunity to strike. (alliteration) _____

_____

4. Bathed in moonlight, the ship sailed for the horizon. (consonance)_____

_____

Application Essay

Writing Workshop

Prewriting

Use the chart below to help plan your application essay. On the left, list some experiences you've had that you feel have been turning points in your life. Below each one, write briefly how you were changed by the experience.

Review the experiences you've listed and choose one that has special meaning for you and has contributed to your personal growth. Put a check in the box by that experience and then answer the questions in the right column.

❑ **Experience:** **How I changed:**	**Why does this experience have special meaning for me?**
❑ **Experience:** **How I changed:**	
❑ **Experience:** **How I changed:**	**What personal qualities, talents, and/or accomplishments does the experience show?**
❑ **Experience:** **How I changed:**	
❑ **Experience:** **How I changed:**	**What is the overall point I want to make about this experience?**

CHAPTER 17

For use with Pupil's Edition pp. 386–391

Application Essay

Writing Workshop

Drafting and Elaboration

The paragraph below is from the second draft of a student's application essay. Help the student make the paragraph less vague and more vivid by following the Suggestions for Elaboration. Refer to the Reader's Notebook and add your own ideas. Write your paragraph on a separate sheet of paper.

Draft

Then between my freshman and sophomore years, my parents separated and divorced. It was a pretty rough time for me and my older sister. It didn't seem to upset my sister. She kept herself busy. She suggested I should do the same.

Suggestions for Elaboration

- Add more specific information about the writer's sister.
- Quote the sister's exact words of advice.
- Clarify any sentences that contradict one another.
- Explain why keeping busy was a good idea for the writer.

READER'S NOTEBOOK

■ Being home was kind of depressing now that the writer's parents were separated and getting divorced. ■ His sister was a "social animal" who was on the cheerleading squad and the swimming team, and who also spent time with her friends. ■ The sister is two years older than the writer, so her advice carries some weight. ■ "Mark," she said, "get a *life*. There's nothing you can do to change things, and you'll be a lot happier if you get out more."

CHAPTER 17

Application Essay

Writing Workshop

Peer Response Guide

Because you are the subject of your application essay, the connection between your experience and how it changed your life is probably obvious to you. But have you made the connection clear enough for your readers? Ask some classmates to read your essay and respond to the following questions.

1. Did the introduction to my essay capture your attention and make you want to read more?

   Response:

   Suggestions for Revision:

2. What achievement or experience is my essay about?

   Response:

   Suggestions for Revision:

3. What important thing did you learn about me from this essay?

   Response:

   Suggestions for Revision:

For use with Pupil's Edition pp. 386–391

CHAPTER 17

Application Essay

Writing Workshop

Peer Response Guide *continued*

4. Why is this achievement or experience important to me?
Response:

Suggestions for Revision:

5. In what places do I not sound like myself?
Response:

Suggestions for Revision:

6. Was anything in my essay confusing or unclear?
Response:

Suggestions for Revision:

CHAPTER 17

Application Essay

Writing Workshop

Revising, Editing, and Proofreading

Revising

TARGET SKILL ➤ Adding Supporting Details

As you revise your application essay, ask yourself the following questions:

- Did I use enough concrete details and examples to make my point stronger and more interesting?
- Is my introduction interesting and engaging?
- Is my essay written in my own voice and from my own experience?
- Did I use a clear, logical organizational pattern?

Editing and Proofreading

TARGET SKILL ➤ Parallel Construction

Refer to the bulleted list below for editing this draft of one student's application essay. Use proofreading marks to correct errors in grammar, usage, mechanics, and spelling. Copy your corrected draft on a separate sheet of paper.

- Use parallel constructions to express ideas that are parallel in meaning.
- Check to make sure that all subjects and verbs agree.
- Whenever possible, combine sentences to make the writing flow more smoothly.
- Delete any sentence that is unnecessary and inconsistent with the tone.

Draft

Everyone in my school, including the weirdest kids, are in some kind of clique. There are the punks and preps, jocks and drama types are another kind, we have motorheads and hippies, and skaters are around, too. I could list groups all day long. For a long time, I thought no one could have crossed over from one group to another unless the clicks were closely related. For example, jocks might also be preps in some special cases. But, basically, jocks are jocks. Geeks have always been geeks.

Applying

Now edit and proofread your own application essay. Refer to the bulleted list above.

For use with Pupil's Edition pp. 386–391

Application Essay

Strong Student Model

Pigeonholes

I am a computer geek. Or rather, I used to see myself as a computer geek. I tell you this right from the start—not because I am ashamed or proud, but because this is how it was. My academic achievements are listed on my transcripts and test scores. However, if you are going to understand me and who I am today, you need to know that to most people I was a computer geek. I no longer see myself that way, though—or in any one way—and that's what I want to write about: How I learned to see beyond such categories.

At my high school, everyone is in a clique. There are punks and preps, jocks and drama types, and so many other groups that an anthropologist could spend her whole career studying us and still not get it right. For a long time, it seemed to me that the borders of these groups were ironclad. Geeks are geeks, and jocks are jocks, and never the twain shall meet.

Then between my freshman and sophomore years, my parents separated and divorced. It was a pretty rough time for me and my older sister, though she seemed to handle it better. She's a social animal and is always out at cheerleading practice, swim meets, or just getting together with friends. <u>"Mark," she said, "get a *life.*</u> <u>There's nothing you can do to change things, and you'll</u> <u>be a lot happier if you get out more."</u>

So I did something I never thought I'd do in a million years: I went to a drama club meeting. A few days later, I went out for track. These were radical changes for me. I had the computer geek physique: pale skin from staying up late working on Web pages, bad hair, and the undeveloped social skills that went with my undeveloped muscles. I have always liked running, though, and I am fast. ("Not fast enough," my track teacher says.) Also, people often say what a clown I am. The practices and club meetings got me out of the house and kept my mind off my parents' divorce.

I discovered I wasn't exceptional at track (I'm not that fast), and my acting skills leave a lot to be desired. (I can play comedy, but put me in a drama and I'm still playing comedy.) And though I like computers, I am not like my die-hard friends who spend whole weekends without seeing real people. Still, I tried. After a while I discovered something I was good at: bringing the different cliques together.

1. The writer uses an intriguing title.

2. Opens with an attention-grabbing statement and describes the theme of the essay.
Other Options:
• Open with a quotation.
• Begin with an anecdote.

3. Uses humor to describe the setting.
Another Option:
• Describe the setting as it is today and tell the events that led up to it.

4. Uses dialogue to place emphasis on an important turning point in the writer's life.

5. Uses exaggeration and humor to reveal interests and abilities.

Application Essay

Strong Student Model *continued*

For example, the drama club videotaped all of its performances. Unfortunately, though, the videos were pretty awful. Most of the actors couldn't tell which end of a video camera is the lens. There was this other group of students at school who were in a video club—dedicated filmmakers. Why not employ them to videotape the drama group? Also, the video club students usually cast themselves in their own movies. This led to performances that made the adjective "wooden" sound like high praise. The drama students were eager to build a video portfolio. Why not cast drama students in those videos? The two groups sounded like an obvious match, but when I suggested they team up, one member of the drama club pretty much summed up the group's attitude: "Work with those dorks? Puh-leeze!" I pushed for it, though. There were a few tense meetings at first, but after a semester the video and drama clubs began to get together regularly.

I didn't stop there, either. My "computer geek" friends make short animated films on their computers. Their audience for these two-minute masterpieces is usually about eight people—parents, friends, and favorite pets. I knew the video club needed help with special effects and titles, so. . . .

All of our efforts resulted in what our faculty advisor praised as the first "high school studio system." Last year we created a ten-minute movie with the participation of five groups, who a year before had despised each other. Our lead was the goalie of the soccer team, who is also a pretty good actor. This magnum opus, "High School Confidential," won first place in the state student film festival.

The most satisfying part for me, though, was what I learned: Even if I am not an exceptional runner, computer jockey, or actor, I can bring people together. I can see the big picture. I will never think of myself—or anybody else—by a mere category name again. <u>Putting someone in a pigeonhole not only sells a person short, it limits their vision</u>. I see that now. In fact, I can see much more than that "computer geek" ever could—or any other person who allows a category to determine who she is or what she can do.

6. Uses vivid details and dialogue to show that achievement was not easily obtained.

7. Shows concrete results of achievement.

8. Conclusion refers back to the title and summarizes the effects of the experience on the writer's life.

9. Needs to correct error in subject-verb agreement.

For use with Pupil's Edition pp. 386–391

CHAPTER 17

Application Essay

Writing Workshop

Average Student Model

The Limits of Geekdom

I am a computer geek.

I am telling you this right from the start not because I am ashamed of being a computer geek, or proud, but that is how my classmates look at me. If you want to know about my academic achievements, you can look at my transcripts and test scores. But if you are going to understand me and who I am today, you need to know that to most people I was a computer geek. At my school, everyone was defined by what group they were in.

Everyone is in a clique. There are punks and preps, jocks and drama types, motorheads and hippies, skaters, and all of the kinds of groups that you can see at any high school. For a long time, it seemed to me that the borders of these groups were ironclad. No one was crossing over from one group to another unless the groups were closely related. For example, jocks might also be preps. But otherwise it was "Geeks are geeks and jocks are jocks and never the twain shall meet."

Then between my freshman and sophomore years, my parents separated and divorced. I know that a lot of people say that divorce is tougher for kids when kids are younger, and that may be true, but all I know is that it was pretty rough on me and my older sister. But it didn't seem to upset my sister much. She keeps herself busy. She suggested I should do the same and get out of the house.

So the next day, I went to a drama club meeting. A few days later, I went out for track. These were serious changes for me. I looked like your usual computer geek. But I have always liked running, and people have often told me what a clown I am. In fact, my clowning around used to get me into worlds of trouble. The practices and club meetings kept me out of the house and kept my mind off of my parents' divorce.

I discovered I wasn't exceptional at track, and my acting skills leave a lot to be desired. And though I like working on computers, I am not like my die-hard friends who spend whole weekends with only their computer. Still, I tried to do my best at each activity. And after a while I discovered something I *could* do: I brought the different cliques together.

1. Uses an intriguing opening statement.

2. Should avoid beginning sentences with *and* or *but* throughout.

3. Does not describe main point of essay—writer's achievement is expanding horizons and moving out of a category.

4. Makes a statement that contradicts previous sentence.

5. Needs to elaborate on statement so that its relevance is clearer.

6. Includes many helpful details, but result is a bit flat and rambling. Addition of vivid words and touches of humor would help.

CHAPTER 17

Application Essay

Average Student Model *continued*

For example, the drama club was videotaping all of its performances. Most actors can't tell which end of a video camera is which or how to light a stage beyond pointing some spotlights and hoping it looks good. But there was a group of student filmmakers at school, and I thought, why not employ them to videotape the drama group? At the same time, I saw that the video students were usually casting themselves in their movies. They were the worst actors imaginable, really awful. The drama students were eager to build a video portfolio, and I thought, why not cast drama students in the videos?

It sounds like an obvious match, but when I suggested the groups team up, <u>everyone on both sides were</u> calling me names and suggesting I get my head checked. There were a few tense meetings at first, but after a semester the video and drama clubs began to get together regularly.

But I didn't stop there. My computer geek friends were making short animated films on their computers, <u>little cartoons with photographs they scan in or else things they draw and then manipulate on screen</u>. Their audience for these two-minute masterpieces was about eight people—parents and friends and so on. But I knew the videographers needed help with special effects and titles, so I suggested they get together.

All of our efforts resulted in a high school movie studio. Last year we created a ten-minute movie with the participation of five different cliques. Our lead actor was the goalie of the soccer team, who we discovered can act. Since the movie was about a soccer player caught up in a scandal, he was an obvious choice. He looked the part. Our magnum opus, "High School Confidential," won first place in the state student film festival.

I learned a lot. I learned how to bring people together across boundaries. I learned never to think of myself—or anybody else—by a mere category name again. And even though my parents got divorced, I had enough going on in my life so that I wasn't as broken up as I might have been.

7. Makes common error in subject/verb agreement.

8. Adds unnecessary elaboration.

9. Adds unnecessary details, and the statement about the soccer goalie looking the part could be misinterpreted.

10. Last sentence detracts from main achievement. Adding vivid words and variety to sentence structure would make conclusion more powerful.

CHAPTER 17

Application Essay

Weak Student Model

Writing Workshop

The Geeks and the Jocks

If you want to know about my academic achievements and stuff, you can look at my transcripts and test scores. But if <u>your</u> going to understand me and who I am today, you need to know that to most people I was a computer geek. I looked like your usual computer geek. At my school, <u>everyone was defined by what group they were in</u>.

Everyone at my school is in a clique. There are the punks and preps, jocks and drama types, motorheads and hippies and skaters. I could list groups all day long. For a long time, I thought no one was crossing over from one group to another unless the groups were closely related. For example, jocks might also be preps in some special cases. But no geeks could be anything but geeks.

Then between my freshman and sophomore years, my parents separated and divorced. I know that a lot of people say that divorce is tougher for kids when kids are younger, and that may be true, but all I know is that it was pretty rough on me and my older sister. <u>But it didn't seem to upset my sister as much</u>. She keeps herself busy. She told me I should do the same and get out of my parents' hair.

I went to a drama club meeting. Then I went out for track. It was scary and a lot of people didn't like me trying out these new activities because I was a computer geek. <u>Not so much my family but people like the jocks and drama types</u>. But I have always liked running, and people like it when I clown around in class. In fact, my clowning around used to get me into worlds of trouble. (<u>Not anymore</u>. I behave now.) The track practices and drama meetings kept my mind off of my parents' divorce.

I wasn't too good at track. I was fine on the relay team, but I couldn't last longer distances and I couldn't jump. And my acting was nothing great either. I could get people to laugh, but that was about it. One play I was in was by Neil Simon, and I think that was the height of my success. My performance had them rolling in the aisles. And even though I said I was a computer geek, and even though I like working on computers, I am not a serious hacker.

1. Title is flat and does not capture essence of essay.

2. Misuses *your* for *you're.*

3. Uses incorrect pronoun *(they);* does not match antecedent *(everyone)* in number.

4. Never states main theme of essay.

5. Needs to rewrite this and several other sentences to avoid beginning with the conjunctions *but* or *and.*

6. Uses sentence fragments rather than complete sentences.

7. Draws reader away from main points by making unnecessary asides.

CHAPTER 17

Application Essay

Writing Workshop

Weak Student Model *continued*

Some of my die-hard friends spend whole weekends with <u>only they're computer</u>. But I tried my best at each activity. And after a while I discovered something I could do: I could get the different cliques to work together.

8. Misuses *they're* for *their.*

For example, the drama club was videotaping all of its performances. They would just put a camera on a tripod and hope it all stayed in focus. Most actors can't tell which end of a video camera is which or how to light a stage beyond pointing some spotlights and hoping it looks good. But I thought, we should get the film club students to videotape the drama group! And the video students were usually acting in their own movies. They were really awful, like the worst movie you've ever seen. I thought, why not cast drama students in the videos?

9. Descriptions of video students' films are probably meant to be humorous, but end up sounding mean. Writer needs lighter touch with humor.

This all sounds pretty obvious, but no one liked my idea. When I suggested it, everyone said no. Most of them were very mean about it. But I asked again. There were a few tense meetings at first, but after a semester the video and drama clubs began to get together regularly.

And I knew my computer geek friends make short animated films on their computers, cool little cartoons with photographs they scan in or else things they draw. These two-minute jokes were seen by about eight people—parents and friends and favorite pets. The video club needed help with things the computer geeks could do, so I suggested they come to one of our meetings.

We practically had a high school movie studio. We created a ten-minute movie with the participation of five different clicks. <u>Our lead actor was the goalie of the soccer team, since the movie was about a soccer player who gets caught in the wrong crowd, he was an obvious choice</u>. He looked the part. "High School Confidential" won first place in the state student film festival.

10. Uses a run-on sentence. Writer's best choice is to delete sentence, since it contains unnecessary and misleading information.

Anyway, I learned a lot from all this and got out of the house more, too.

11. Essay lacks a conclusion that summarizes main points and explains how experience affected the writer.

For use with Pupil's Edition pp. 386–391

CHAPTER 17

Application Essay

Writing Workshop

Rubric for Evaluation

Ideas and Content	Weak	Average	Strong
1. Reflects a thoughtful response to the application prompt			
2. Identifies and describes a significant experience or event			
3. Explains what the experience or achievement means to the writer			
4. Has an engaging title and introduction			
5. Comes from the writer's own experience			

Structure and Form			
6. Is written in the writer's own voice and style			
7. Reflects careful attention to grammar, style, and organization			

Grammar, Usage, and Mechanics			
8. Contains no more than two or three minor errors in spelling, capitalization, and punctuation			
9. Contains no more than two or three minor errors in grammar and usage			

Writing Progress to Date (Writing Portfolio)

The strongest aspect of this writing is _____

_____

The final version shows improvement over the rough draft in this way: _____

_____

A specific improvement over past assignments in your portfolio is _____

_____

A skill to work on in future assignments is _____

_____

Additional comments: _____

_____

CHAPTER 17

Personality Profile

Prewriting

Before you write your personality profile, you need to gather information about your subject. Use the following chart to list what you already know about the person and the questions you still have. Refer to the chart to plan your research or to formulate questions for an interview.

Physical Appearance	
Accomplishments	
Setting	
Anecdotes/Quotes	
My Feelings Toward Subject	
Questions I Have	

CHAPTER 18

For use with Pupil's Edition pp. 394–399

Personality Profile

Writing Workshop

Drafting and Elaboration

Details help to create a rounded profile of a subject. The paragraph below is from a draft of one student's personality profile. Add details to the paragraph by following the Suggestions for Elaboration. You can use information from the Reader's Notebook or add your own ideas. Write your paragraph on a separate sheet of paper.

Draft

Tiger watched his father hit golf balls. He imitated his father. He appeared on a television show. He began to break records. This was when he was two and three years old. Then, he was older. And he began winning amateur championships. His father was a golfer, too.

Suggestions for Elaboration

- Provide more details about how Tiger learned to imitate his father.
- Explain the relevance of the fact that Tiger's father was a golfer.
- Provide examples of records that Tiger broke.
- Clarify the ages at which Tiger achieved his accomplishments.

READER'S NOTEBOOK

■ Tiger's father was also an excellent golfer. ■ While still in his crib, Tiger watched his father hit golf balls into a net. ■ Tiger began imitating his father's golf swing before he was out of his high chair. ■ When Tiger was three, he shot 48 for nine holes. ■ He began winning amateur championships when he was eight. ■ At age 21, he became the youngest Masters champion in history.

Personality Profile

Writing Workshop

Peer Response Guide

You are very familiar with the subject of your personality profile, but will your reader develop a good understanding of the person? To find out if you've been successful in bringing your subject to life, ask a peer reviewer questions like the ones below.

1. What impression did you get of my subject?

Response:

Suggestions for Revision:

2. What details made the person most real to you?

Response:

Suggestions for Revision:

3. What details distracted you?

Response:

Suggestions for Revision:

For use with Pupil's Edition pp. 394–399

CHAPTER 18

Personality Profile

Writing Workshop

Peer Response Guide *continued*

4. What do you think my attitude toward the person is?

Response:

Suggestions for Revision:

5. Did my beginning draw you into the profile, and did my ending give a sense of completeness?

Response:

Suggestions for Revision:

6. What more would you like to know about the person?

Response:

Suggestions for Revision:

CHAPTER 18

Personality Profile

Revising, Editing, and Proofreading

Revising

TARGET SKILL ➤ Using Dialogue

When revising your personality profile, ask yourself the following questions:

- Do the characters' words sound natural? Do they reveal the characters' personalities?
- Have I used details, dialogue, and/or descriptions to create a vivid impression of the person?
- Have I conveyed why the person is important to me?
- Have I created a unified tone and impression?

Editing and Proofreading

TARGET SKILL ➤ Pronoun-Antecedent Agreement

Use the bulleted suggestions below to edit this paragraph from a student's draft of a personality profile. Proofread by correcting errors in grammar, usage, mechanics, and spelling. Copy your corrected draft on a separate sheet of paper.

- Correct pronouns so they agree with their antecedents in person, number, and gender.
- Change sentence fragments so that they express complete thoughts.
- Avoid repetitious words and phrases.
- Make sure verb tense is consistent.

Draft

Tiger grew up hearing stories of Tiger Phong. Phong was his fathers best friend who he had fought with during the vietnam war. After they ended his father lost contact with his friend. His father thought he could get in touch with his friend to tell him about the birth of Tiger Woods. But no. His father's friend dies just eight months after Tiger is borne.

Applying

Now edit and proofread your own personality profile. Refer to the bulleted list above.

For use with Pupil's Edition pp. 394–399

CHAPTER 18

Personality Profile

Strong Student Model

Writing Workshop
*These writing models are also available in **Assessment Masters**.*

A Tiger on the Golf Course

Every now and then, exceptional people—athletes, artists, and performers—burst upon the world in a dazzle of talent. Tiger Woods is such a person. At 22 years of age, Tiger has blasted career records of several established golfers and promises to continue with this trend.

Tiger was a child prodigy. While still in the crib, he watched his father hit golf balls into a net and, before he was out of the high chair, according to his father, was imitating his swing. At the age of two, he appeared on a television show, putting with Bob Hope. When he was three, he shot 48 for nine holes. Trained by his father, an excellent golfer, he began winning amateur championships when he was just eight years old.

Tiger (his real name is Eldrick) grew up in Southern California, the son of a Thai woman and an African-American veteran of the Vietnam War. Of his unique ethnic heritage, he says, "I feel very fortunate, and equally proud, to be both African-American and Asian. . . . [but] I hope I can just be a golfer and a human being." It hasn't been easy. Because of his ethnic background, Tiger has sometimes gotten more attention than he has liked.

Tiger played in his first professional tournament at age 16. When he was just 21 years old, he became the youngest Masters champion in history. No African American or Asian had ever won the Masters championship—he was the first. Throughout his career, he has wowed fans and pros alike. As Jack Nicklaus said, "There isn't a flaw in his golf or his makeup. He will win more majors than Arnold Palmer and me combined. Somebody is going to dust my records. It might as well be Tiger, because he's such a great kid."

I especially admire Tiger Woods because he doesn't let success go to his head. "Golf is not everything," he says. "It never will be. The most important thing is furthering yourself, making yourself a better person."

1. The writer immediately establishes interest with intriguing title and details.
Other Options:
• Begin with a quotation.
• Provide historical context.

2. The writer uses lively details and anecdotes to create a complex portrait. Includes transitional words and phrases.

3. Quotes the subject, revealing personality and creating a vivid impression.

4. Conveys why the writer admires the subject.

5. Ends with a direct statement of personal values by the subject, providing a sense of completeness.

CHAPTER 18

Personality Profile

Writing Workshop

Average Student Model

Tiger Woods: A Talented Young Golfer

There are some extremely talented people in the world, such as athletes, artists, and performers. Tiger Woods is one of them. At 22 years of age, Tiger was already making more than $2 million a year as a professional golfer. He has broken career records of several established golfers. He will probably be continuing to do this in the future.

1. The writer begins with intriguing details, but the sentence structure could be varied to create more interest.

Tiger was a child prodigy. <u>That means he was already doing things when he was a kid that most people don't do until they're grown up</u>. When he was still a baby, he watched his father hit golf balls into a net and then started imitating his swing. At the age of two, he appeared on a television show, putting with Bob Hope. When he was three, he shot 48 for nine holes. He began winning amateur championships when he was just eight years old. His father trained him.

2. Provides an unnecessary definition.

Tiger grew up in Southern California, the son of a Thai woman and an African-American veteran of the Vietnam War. His real name is Eldrick. He says, "I feel very fortunate, and equally proud, to be both African-American and Asian. . . . [but] I hope I can just be a golfer and a human being." It hasn't been easy. Because of his ethnic background, Tiger has gotten lots and lots of attention.

Tiger played in his first professional tournament at age 16. At age 21, he became the youngest Masters champion. No African American or Asian had won the Masters championship. Throughout his career, he has wowed fans and pros alike. Jack Nicklaus said, "There isn't a flaw in his golf or his makeup. He will win more majors than Arnold Palmer and me combined. Somebody is going to dust my records. It might as well be Tiger, because he's such a great kid."

3. Quotation from competitor reveals how others see the subject.

Tiger's talent is amazing to someone like me who can hardly play golf. But I think the way he thinks is really cool, too. Tiger loves golf. But he says it's not everything, that it's more important to make yourself a better person.

4. Tells why writer admires subject, but the second sentence is repetitive and uses slang.

5. Ends with a paraphrase rather than a direct quote, which might be more effective.

Personality Profile

Weak Student Model

Golfer Tiger Woods

There are some very talented people in the world, such as athletes, artists, and performers. Tiger Woods is one of these talented people. Tiger made more than $2 million a year as a professional golfer, beginning when he was about 22. He has broken career records of several established golfers. Probably, he will keep doing that.

Tiger watched his father hit golf balls. He imitated his father. He appeared on a television show. He began to break records. This was when he was two and three years old. Then, he was older. And he began winning amateur championships. His father was a golfer, too.

Tiger grew up in Southern California. His mother was Thai and his father was African-American. his father was a veteran of the Vietnam War. His father is a golfer, too. "I feel very fortunate, and equally proud, to be both African-American and Asian. . . . [but] I hope I can just be a golfer and a human being." That's not easy, though. Because of his parents, Tiger has gotten lots of attention— way too much.

Tiger played in his first professional tournament at age 16. When he was just 21 years old, he became a Masters champion. No one had ever been so young and won the Masters championship. No African American or Asian had won the Masters championship. Fans and pros all think he is a great player.

One golfer said, "There isn't a flaw in his golf or his makeup. He will win more majors than Arnold Palmer and me combined. Somebody is going to dust my records. It might as well be Tiger, because he's such a great kid."

"Golf is not everything. It never will be." Tiger is philosophikal about his talent and success. The most important thing is to make yourself a better person. I think that's why he is especially cool.

1. The writer begins with intriguing details, but the sentence structure could be varied to create interest.

2. Again, sentence structure could be varied.
Other Options:
• Clarify when events occurred.
• Be specific about subject's age.

3. There is an error in capitalization.

4. It is not clear who is making the statement.

5. The two paragraphs could be combined into one.
Other Options:
• Identify the speaker.
• Vary sentence structure.

6. The topic sentence of the paragraph is incorrectly placed.

7. There is an error in spelling.

Personality Profile

Writing Workshop

Rubric for Evaluation

Ideas and Content	Weak	Average	Strong
1. Uses dialogue when appropriate			
2. Uses descriptions, details, and anecdotes to create a vivid impression of the person			
3. Puts the person in context to reveal the subject's personality			
4. Conveys why the person is important to the writer			
5. Captures readers' interest and leaves them with a sense of completeness			

Structure and Form			
6. Creates a unified tone and impression			
7. Uses a logical pattern of organization			

Grammar, Usage, and Mechanics			
8. Contains no more than two or three minor errors in spelling, capitalization, and punctuation			
9. Contains no more than two or three minor errors in grammar and usage			

Writing Progress to Date (Writing Portfolio)

The strongest aspect of this writing is_____

_____

The final version shows improvement over the rough draft in this way:_____

_____

A specific improvement over past assignments in your portfolio is_____

_____

A skill to work on in future assignments is_____

_____

Additional comments: _____

_____

For use with Pupil's Edition pp. 394–399

Critical Review of Literature

Writing Workshop

Prewriting

To write a critical review, choose a literary work you like or one you strongly dislike. After selecting a work, use the chart below to analyze its most important elements. For a novel or short story, examine the elements of theme, characters, plot, and setting. For a drama, include dialogue and action. For a poem, include rhythm and language. List specific examples in the work that support your critique of each element. After examining the elements, focus your review on one or two of them.

Element	Critique	Supporting Evidence

CHAPTER 19

Critical Review of Literature

Writing Workshop

Drafting and Elaboration

The passage below is from a draft of a critical review of James Joyce's story "The Dead." It does not include enough details and examples. Make the paragraph more vivid by following the Suggestions for Elaboration. Use information from the Reader's Notebook or add your own ideas. Write your paragraph on a separate sheet of paper.

Draft

While Gabriel was looking at his wife he began to think about how everybody was dying, how life was a long process that ended in death. He was also thinking about all of the people he knew who had died or were going to die. Then he got carried away thinking about the snow that was falling on everyone and everything.

Suggestions for Elaboration

- Explain why "looking at his wife" makes Gabriel think of death.
- Identify some of the people he thinks about.
- Quote from the story to provide supporting evidence.
- Clarify what is meant by saying that Gabriel "got carried away."

READER'S NOTEBOOK

■ Gabriel looks at his wife, Gretta, as she sleeps, and he notices that she is aging. ■ He thinks about the long-dead boy, Michael Furey, who had loved her. ■ He thinks about his old Aunt Julia who will soon die. ■ It seems to him that "one by one they were all becoming shades." ■ Gabriel's reverie becomes a kind of vision. ■ He imagines the snow falling all over Ireland, falling upon the cemeteries, falling "upon all the living and the dead."

For use with Pupil's Edition pp. 402–407

CHAPTER 19

Critical Review of Literature

Writing Workshop

Peer Response Guide

It may be difficult to know if a critical review has achieved its desired purpose. To find out if you have successfully communicated what you intended, ask a classmate to read your critical review and answer the following questions.

1. What is my overall opinion of this literary work?

Response:

Suggestions for Revision:

2. What elements of this work did I analyze? Should I have analyzed any other elements?

Response:

Suggestions for Revision:

3. What criteria did I use? Is it appropriate to the work I evaluated?

Response:

Suggestions for Revision:

Critical Review of Literature

Writing Workshop

Peer Response Guide *continued*

4. Did I miss any important standards for evaluating the work? If so, which other ones could I have used?

Response:

Suggestions for Revision:

5. What supporting evidence was most convincing? least convincing?

Response:

Suggestions for Revision:

6. What details, if any, would have supported my opinion better?

Response:

Suggestions for Revision:

For use with Pupil's Edition pp. 402–407

Critical Review of Literature

Writing Workshop

Revising, Editing, and Proofreading

Revising

TARGET SKILL ➤ Elaborating with Facts and Examples

As you revise your critical review, ask yourself the following questions:

• Have I provided concrete details and examples to illustrate my point?

• Have I identified and briefly described the work I'm writing about?

• Have I stated my opinions clearly?

• Have I stated the criteria by which I judge the work?

Editing and Proofreading

TARGET SKILL ➤ Subject-Verb Agreement

Use the bulleted suggestions below to edit this paragraph from a student's draft of a review of "The Dead." Use proofreading marks to correct errors in grammar, spelling, usage, and mechanics.

• Check to be sure that all subjects and verbs agree.

• Rephrase sentences to eliminate unnecessary words.

• Correct any run-on sentences or sentence fragments.

• Make sure that pronouns agree with their antecedents.

Draft

Gabriel looked at his wife while she was sleeping and noticed that his wife have aged. He thought about Michael Furey, once the sweetheart of his wife. Long dead. One wet and stormy night, the sickly young man had came to her garden, losing his life as a result. Gabriel also thought about those others who had died or were soon to die, he thought especially about his aunt Julia. Then his imaginnation created a larger vision. He had a vision of all the living and the dead, with the snow falling on it.

Applying

Now edit and proofread your own critical review. Refer to the bulleted list above.

Critical Review of Literature

Writing Workshop

These writing models are also available in **Assessment Masters**.

Strong Student Model

"The Dead"

On the surface, James Joyce's story "The Dead" is the tale of a grand party. In a way, it might be thought of as the grand party of life itself because by the end of the story the reader has been powerfully reminded that the party of life inevitably ends in death. In the frequent mentions of death and of the passing of a generation, and in the final scenes of the story when the memory of a dead young man comes between Gabriel and his wife Gretta, the theme of the universality of death takes on several different shades of meaning.

The power of the theme, the realism with which the plot, characters, and setting contribute to the thematic development, and the subtlety with which the ideas are expressed are the standards by which the reader can judge the success of "The Dead." By these standards, Joyce's story is truly excellent.

Joyce uses the literary technique of having an omniscient narrator describe the scene in vivid detail. The story opens with the party already in full swing: "Lily, the caretaker's daughter, was literally run off her feet." Like Lily, the reader is swept away by a list of people and place names, a confusing tidal wave of information about pianos and food and singers and voices, many voices, people talking about all sorts of things. The reader doesn't yet realize who and what the story is about.

Then the main character, Gabriel, arrives with his wife, Gretta. Hints of mortality arrive with them. Gabriel complains that his wife took "three mortal hours" to dress herself, and someone comments that in the wintry weather the two "must be perished alive." Already Joyce's theme of how we are "all becoming shades" is present. Later, this theme is expanded upon by Gabriel himself, when in his dinner speech he comments that "a new generation" should "still cherish in our hearts the memory of those dead and gone great ones." Throughout the story, there are mentions of different generations, of "Mary Jane's pupils" as well as old Aunt Julia, who Gabriel realizes will soon die. Before the reader is even aware of the theme, it is present, shaping the story and foreshadowing the climax.

1. Identifies the work and the author. Introduces the writer's interpretation of the story's theme; offers preview of the story to support that interpretation.

2. Clearly states three criteria for judging work and states critical opinion of it.

3. Uses quotation and description to support analysis of Joyce's technique.

4. Uses several quotations as evidence to show how skillfully Joyce suggests the theme.

5. Sums up evidence and draws a conclusion to support the main idea of this paragraph.

For use with Pupil's Edition pp. 402–407

Critical Review of Literature

Strong Student Model *continued*

At home after the party, Gabriel discovers that his wife still mourns for a dead lover. Here all the threads in the story come together. Gretta has heard a man at the party singing a song called "The Lass of Aughrim," and she recalls a young man who once used to sing that song. She had loved the young man, who, she tells Gabriel, died for her at the age of seventeen. The young man, who was very ill, had come to her garden on a wet, stormy night to declare his despair at her departure for convent school and his desire to die. "So she had had that romance in her life: a man had died for her sake," Gabriel thinks. "How poor a part he, her husband, had played in her life," he thinks. Her first love's sacrifice is one he can never compete with, and all of Gabriel's pompous posturings at the party seem empty to him when he realizes how little he knew his own wife.

Then the story changes, and the narration seems to merge with Gabriel's own thoughts. The realism of the party and homecoming falls away in Gabriel's reverie about the story's true subject: death, the inevitable end that we all come to sooner or later. He looks at his sleeping wife and sees beyond his pettiness. He sees that she has aged and that her face is "no longer the face for which Michael Furey had braved death." Then his thoughts touch upon his Aunt Julia, and how "one by one they were all becoming shades." Finally his vision encompasses all of Ireland, including those dead buried in cemeteries. The story ends with visions of snow falling "upon all the living and the dead." The snow is falling equally upon everyone, shrouding everything without regard for life or death. In this passage the reader forgets the omniscient narrator and, instead, seems to be seeing the vision through Gabriel's eyes. Like Gabriel, the reader must acknowledge and live with the past and the future.

"The Dead" is the final story in Joyce's collection *Dubliners* (1914), and it is a fitting close. It has characters whose actions and feelings the reader cares about—characters drawn with all the ambiguity of real life. It has a powerful, artistically developed theme. And these elements converge in a memorable vision and a central insight that the reader has been brought to share.

6. Quotations support the writer's analysis of the characters.

7. Shows how change in Joyce's style—from realism to reverie—contributes to development of the theme.

8. Restates criteria and offers a persuasive judgment on the story's worth.

Critical Review of Literature

Writing Workshop

Average Student Model

"The Dead"

James Joyce's story "The Dead" is the tale of a large party and its aftermath. It is only on reading about the aftermath of the party, however, that the reader can see that the story is about much more than a lively party. It is about death and about how we live our lives in the shadow of the dead people we have known. This theme works on several levels: first in the notion of the way death is all around us—even while at a party; then, when the ghost of a dead boy comes between the main character, Gabriel, and his wife, Gretta; and finally in Gabriel's insight about how we are "all becoming shades," an insight that allows him to state Joyce's theme.

A short story can be judged according to how convincing the characters are and how well the theme is brought to light. By these standards, "The Dead" is a very good story.

The story opens with the annual party already in full swing, and from the opening paragraphs we learn that the party is "always a great affair." Indeed, soon the reader is overwhelmed with the names of characters (Lily, Miss Kate, Miss Julia, Pat, Mr. Fulham, and on and on), and of dishes ("diamond-bone sirloins, three-shilling tea, and the best bottled stout"), and of details of the large house (there is a piano, and at least two floors, and a ballroom of some sort). The reader feels like a partygoer, caught in a swirl of activity. It is so busy that it is easy to miss the presence of death at one's elbow.

Then the main character, Gabriel, arrives with his wife, Gretta. The first mentions of death arrive with them. Gabriel says that his wife took "three mortal hours" to dress herself, and someone else says that the two "must be perished alive" from the cold. Already Joyce's theme of how we are "all becoming shades" is sounded, but because the reader isn't looking for it, these references go by unnoticed. Later, even Gabriel talks about death when in his dinner speech he comments that "a new generation" should "still cherish in our hearts the memory of those dead and gone great ones." Throughout the story, there are mentions of different generations, of "Mary Jane's pupils" as well as of old Aunt Julia, who Gabriel thinks will die soon. So

1. Identifies the work and author. Interprets and elaborates on the story's theme.

2. States two simple criteria for judging the work; states critical opinion.

3. Uses description and quotations to show setting.

4. Final sentence recalls the theme and provides good transition to the next paragraph.

5. Uses quotations to support interpretation of the theme.

For use with Pupil's Edition pp. 402–407

Critical Review of Literature

Writing Workshop

Average Student Model *continued*

though the reader is not even aware of the theme, it is present.

But after the party the story changes and becomes more serious, and the theme becomes more central to the story. When they have gone home, Gabriel discovers that his wife still longs for a dead boy she knew when she was in her teens. At the party Gretta had heard a man singing a song called "The Lass of Aughrim," and it has made her sad. When Gabriel asks her about this, she recalls a young man she loved who, she says, died for her. He had been sick and had waited outside her window in the cold, and he caught his death that way. Because of the song, the dead boy's ghost is present in a way, coming between Gabriel and Gretta. Her first love's sacrifice is one Gabriel can never compete with. He thought he was her only love, but he was dead wrong.

Then the story changes again, the theme taking over the story in a way that is surprising since the first part of the story feels different in tone and style. Gabriel, who at first was angry at his wife for betraying him (even if it was only by thinking of a ghost), forgives her and even that dead boy. He is ashamed of himself. Everyone is dying, he thinks, and he looks at his wife as she sleeps and sees she has aged. He thinks about his Aunt Julia, and how "one by one they were all becoming shades." Soon the dead are crowding into his vision, and by the end of the story his vision includes all the dead in Ireland, lying in their cemeteries, as well as all the people who are on the way to death.

With this new understanding, Gabriel embodies the theme of the story, a theme that Joyce has been hinting at all along with the frequent references to death as well as with the appearance of the dead Michael Furey when Gretta hears "The Lass of Aughrim." Along with Gabriel, the reader gets the main idea that has been buried in the story all along. In "The Dead," Joyce succeeds in making the reader appreciate his characters and his theme.

6. Draws a conclusion that supports main idea of paragraph.

7. Describes central episode of story. Lacks supporting quotations.

8. Describes concluding episode but could do so more clearly. Repeats earlier quotation to reinforce interpretation of theme.

9. Recapitulates theme. Concludes with one-sentence restatement of criteria and critical opinion. Needs stronger conclusion.

Critical Review of Literature

Writing Workshop

Weak Student Model

"The Dead"

James Joyce's story "The Dead" is about a big party and a pompous <u>guy</u> who attends it with his wife. The story works by <u>pulling the rug out from under</u> the main character, Gabriel, when Gabriel discovers he wasn't his wife's first lover. The title "The Dead" refers to her first lover and also to the theme of the story, which is that the dead are always with us (<u>as my grandfater likes to say</u>). Though this theme isn't clear until the end of the story, Joyce is working it throughout, beginning with the title, then continuing with little hints he drops along the way, and finally with the revelation by Gabriel's wife. All of these techniques make it clear by the end of the story what Joyce is up to, and the reader—along with Gabriel—figures out the theme.

I judge a story according to how interesting the characters are, how lively the action is, how clear the meaning is, and how realistic and believable the whole thing is.

The title of the story, "The Dead," was at first pretty confusing. If anything, the story seemed to be about the living. There was the big party, and there was dancing and singing, and even some drinking (though everyone frowned on the guys who drink), and death seemed to be the farthest thing from the characters' minds. But the title alerts the reader to the theme of the story, and so while we read we are looking for hints of death and trying to connect up the title with the story.

The story opens with the party already happening. "Lily," Joyce wrote, "was literally run off her feet." <u>Meaning that the maid was so busy that she was swept off her feet by all the activity</u>. That phrase, "run off her feet," brought to mind immediately something bad happening to Lily, like maybe she'd be hit by a car. Then Gabriel arrived with his wife, Gretta. And Joyce started mentioning death. Gabriel said that his wife took three "mortal" hours to dress herself, and someone else said that the two of them must be "perished" from the cold. Already Joyce's theme of how death is all around us was there in the story, but the reader isn't looking for it and so doesn't notice. Later, even Gabriel talked about people dying and young ones taking their place when in his

1. Identifies the work and author in first sentence. Diction is too informal throughout. Tone is inappropriately flippant.

2. Offers somewhat vague interpretation of story's theme. Previews the story to support the interpretation; makes good point about the title.

3. Briefly states four criteria but doesn't include a critical evaluation.

4. Uses sentence fragment, followed by an unlikely interpretation of a detail in the story.

5. Uses description and quotations to show how Joyce suggests theme.

For use with Pupil's Edition pp. 402–407

Critical Review of Literature

Writing Workshop

Weak Student Model *continued*

dinner speech he said that "a new generation" should "still cherish in our hearts the memory of those dead and gone great ones."

Pretty soon Joyce gives us an example of someone who died but who was still hanging around among the living. Gabriel was ready to leave when he saw his wife standing on the stairs listening to someone sing. She was listening to a song called "The Lass of Aughrim," and it made her sad, but to Gabriel's mind she looked like she was full of love for him. He couldn't have been more wrong. She was actually thinking of a boy who loved her when she was a teenager. This boy was sick but came out in the cold rain to wait for her, and he died a week later. Learning that he was only second in his wife's love life made Gabriel question himself and their marriage. He realized that his wife's reactions in her life were as much because of the dead boy as they were because of Gabriel himself. This also shows the theme at work, since for Gretta the dead was with her, and as she once told Gabriel, the dead was with him, too.

Then the story got really strange. Gabriel's wife fell asleep, and while he was looking at her he began to think about how everybody was dying, how life was a long process that ended in death. He was also thinking about all of the people he knew who died or are going to die. Then he started thinking about the snow falling on everyone equally, alive or dead, and that maybe there wasn't such a big difference in the end. He almost has a vision, all the snow falling on the whole world.

If the reader hasn't figured out what was going on in the story before Gabriel's vision, by the end of the story the theme was clear. Because of the title, because of how references to death and the dead keep popping up in the story, and because of Gretta's final revelation about dead Michael Furey, the theme is pretty clearly laid out. And in the last line, the story has moved from a happening party to a quiet snowfall on graves, so that even the dullest reader can see how Joyce has led us from the high points of life (a party) to the end of life. Like Gabriel, we think about death and realize it is with us everywhere we look.

Joyce told a pretty good story about Gabriel and Gretta and her past history, and he certainly made the theme clear, but his style was inconsistent. It started out to be realistic and finally became weird and abstract.

CHAPTER 19

6. Summarizes central discovery in story. Could have used supporting quotations.

7. Summarizes final scene, again without quotations. Offers critical judgment that scene is "strange," but doesn't relate judgment to criteria.

8. Restates interpretation of story's theme, summarizing evidence.

9. Briefly states critical judgment based on earlier criteria.

CHAPTER 1

Critical Review of Literature

Writing Workshop

Rubric for Evaluation

Ideas and Content	Weak	Average	Strong
1. Identifies the work being reviewed			
2. Briefly tells what the work is about			
3. States the writer's opinions clearly			
4. States the criteria by which the writer judged the work			
5. Uses enough details from the work to support the review			
6. Summarizes the writer's opinion			

Structure and Form			
7. Uses quotations correctly			
8. Includes transitions to show relationships between ideas			

Grammar, Usage, and Mechanics			
9. Contains no more than two or three minor errors in spelling, capitalization, and punctuation			
10. Contains no more than two or three minor errors in grammar and usage			

Writing Progress to Date (Writing Portfolio)

The strongest aspect of this writing is _____

_____

The final version shows improvement over the rough draft in this way: _____

_____

A specific improvement over past assignments in your portfolio is _____

_____

A skill to work on in future assignments is _____

_____

Additional comments: _____

_____

For use with Pupil's Edition pp. 402–407

Subject Analysis

Writing Workshop

Prewriting

After completing the research on your topic, use the outline below to plan your subject analysis. Decide who your audience will be and whether your analysis will inform, persuade, amuse, or serve some other purpose. Express your main idea in one or two sentences. Then briefly describe the important parts of your subject, and supply supporting details for each part.

SUBJECT ANALYSIS PLAN

Topic: _____

Audience and Purpose: _____

_____

Main Idea: _____

_____

Part 1: _____

Supporting Details: _____

_____

_____

_____

Part 2: _____

Supporting Details: _____

_____

_____

_____

Part 3: _____

Supporting Details: _____

_____

_____

_____

Subject Analysis

Drafting and Elaboration

The paragraph below is a first draft from an essay analyzing the need for safe driving. Develop the ideas in the draft using the Suggestions for Elaboration, the information from the Reader's Notebook, and your own ideas. Write your paragraph on a separate sheet of paper.

Draft

A lot of drivers let their minds wander. They may be thinking about something other than their driving. Sometimes drivers try to do two things at once. They do all kinds of bizarre things when they should be paying attention to their driving. Then they make mistakes that can have disastrous consequences. Such mistakes could cost them their lives—or someone else's life.

Suggestions for Elaboration

- Explain what distracted drivers may be thinking about.
- Describe some of the bizarre things drivers do in their cars.
- Give examples of mistakes distracted drivers might make.
- Add more information about the consequences of driving while distracted.

READER'S NOTEBOOK

■ A driver may be thinking about a problem at work, an algebra exam at school, Friday's party, or Saturday's game. ■ You see drivers applying mascara, combing their hair, conducting an unseen orchestra, turning around to talk to someone in the back seat, chatting on the phone, or even shaving. ■ They might run a stoplight or a stop sign. ■ They might fail to slow down at a dangerous curve or intersection. ■ Consequences could range from a traffic ticket or a dented fender to a major accident— from bumps and bruises to a tragic fatality.

For use with Pupil's Edition pp. 410–415

Subject Analysis

Peer Response Guide

You know the points you want to make in your subject analysis, but will they be clear to the reader? Find out how close your first draft comes to fulfilling your goals. Ask a peer reviewer to read your draft and answer the questions below.

1. What is the main idea I am trying to communicate?

   Response:

   Suggestions for Revision:

2. How engaging is my introduction? Does it suggest what is to come?

   Response:

   Suggestions for Revision:

3. What did you find most interesting about my subject?

   Response:

   Suggestions for Revision:

Subject Analysis

Writing Workshop

Peer Response Guide *continued*

4. What could I add to my analysis to make it clearer?

Response:

Suggestions for Revision:

5. What terms need definitions or explanations?

Response:

Suggestions for Revision:

6. How strong is my conclusion? Does my analysis support this conclusion?

Response:

Suggestions for Revision:

For use with Pupil's Edition pp. 410–415

Subject Analysis

Writing Workshop

Revising, Editing, and Proofreading

Revising
TARGET SKILL ➤ Crafting Effective Introductions

When revising your subject analysis, ask yourself the following questions:

- Is my introduction effective, informative, and engaging?
- Have I identified the parts that compose the subject?
- Did I examine and explain each part and show how the parts relate to the whole subject and support the main idea or thesis?
- Have I presented the information in a logical order?

Editing and Proofreading
TARGET SKILL ➤ Correcting Dangling Modifiers

Refer to the bulleted list below to edit this paragraph from a student's first draft of an analysis on safe driving. Use proofreading marks to correct errors in grammar, usage, mechanics, and spelling. Copy your corrected draft on a separate sheet of paper.

- Correct any dangling or misplaced modifiers by placing them closer to the words they modify.
- Check to make sure that sentence parts parallel in meaning are also parallel in construction.
- Make sure that pronouns match their antecedents in number.
- Make sure that subjects and verbs agree.

Draft

Drivers often think their car parts are in fine condition, so they neglect maintenance. Don't trust to luck. Have the engine, brakes, lights and tires check by a mechanic. Keep each window clean so they give you the best possible visibility. Play your radio softly or it should be turned off if it becomes a distraction. Then pay attention to traffic and pedestrians when driving. You never knows whos life you might save.

Applying

Now edit and proofread your own subject analysis. Refer to the bulleted list above.

CHAPTER 20

Subject Analysis

Strong Student Model

Defensive Driving

Does this sound familiar? You're stuck in rush-hour traffic. You've left school after soccer practice and are late for work. In your narrow lane on the freeway, cars are creeping slowly past the scene of an auto accident. You can't resist rubbernecking, either. When you reach the accident site, you look out the window and see paramedics working over an unconscious woman. Is she dead? you wonder. Is she in shock? Perhaps if you had left soccer practice fifteen minutes earlier, that would be you lying on the ground. Still looking, still wondering, you are startled out of your reverie by a loud crash. You've just run into the car in front of you!

Fortunately, neither you nor the other driver is hurt, but imagine what might have happened if you had been traveling at 60, 70, even 80 miles an hour!

We spend so much time in cars that we forget we are traveling in enormous, heavy hunks of steel, inches from other vehicles, often hurtling along at fast speeds. We face bad weather, bad road conditions, and many distractions. We can't change the driving habits of other drivers, but we can change our own. Defensive driving saves lives and even lowers insurance rates. Here are some suggestions.

The first rule of defensive driving is to slow down and put some space between you and other cars on the road. Ideally, there should be one car's length for every ten miles per hour of speed between automobiles. This distance should be increased at night and in bad weather. Pay attention to the posted speed limits, but go with the flow of traffic. If everyone around you is going well over the speed limit, increase your speed at least a little so that you do not inadvertently become a hazard.

Second, never operate a vehicle unless you are fully alert, and never get in a car with an impaired driver. Remember that more than half of all accidents are caused by drunk drivers. Be careful about taking certain medications that might make you drowsy. Also, be especially cautious for signs of impairment in other drivers on the road, such as erratic driving.

1. The writer introduces the subject with an interesting, real-life example.

Other Options:
- Pose a question.
- Present a startling, unusual, or interesting fact.

2. Introduces the main idea or thesis and signals the organizational structure.

3. Identifies the first rule of defensive driving and supports this part of the analysis with examples.

For use with Pupil's Edition pp. 410–415

Subject Analysis

Strong Student Model *continued*

Another cause of accidents is bad road conditions. If you are approaching a construction site, slow down and keep your eyes open for heavy equipment, signalers, or obstructions in the road. No matter where or when you are driving, remember to think ahead and be ready to stop or take evasive action at a moment's notice. This means to always keep your eyes on the road and to check the rearview mirror frequently. Look for other vehicles, bicycles, and children in the road. Slow down when approaching an intersection, even if the light is green. You never know what the other guy is going to do!

4. Identifies additional components of the analysis and provides examples. Uses transitional words and phrases.

Make sure that the vehicle you are driving is in tip-top shape. Check the engine, brakes, lights, and tires frequently. Wash your windows so that you have clear visibility all around. Make sure that your seat belt is in good working order, and get in the habit of strapping yourself in as soon as you get in the car.

We all like to drive and listen to music, but sometimes it can be hazardous. Loud music may prevent you from hearing sirens or honking horns warning you of danger. You may get so caught up in the music that you forget you are steering a two-ton killer at top speeds. Remember, too, that fumbling to rewind a tape or change a radio station may distract your attention from the road.

5. Identifies the last part—the competence of other drivers.

Finally, it's always a good rule of thumb to remember that most people are merely adequate drivers, and many are downright incompetent. People do the strangest things in cars. They eat, they shave, they light cigarettes, they read maps, they talk on the phone, they address envelopes or scribble notes to themselves, they comb their hair, they put on makeup and lipstick, they adjust their mirrors and their seats, they keep up running conversations with people riding in the back seats. They don't signal or brake. They change lanes without looking. They run stop signs and red lights. Watch out for them!

6. Repeats the pronoun they, which slows down the pace too much. Also, the list of examples could be shortened by combining ideas (e.g., "makeup" instead of "makeup and lipstick").

This is just an introduction to some of the principles of defensive driving. There's a lot more to learn about defensive driving from courses that are offered in most cities. Defensive driving may not earn you any "cool" points with your friends, but it may very well save their lives, and your own. You decide.

7. The writer concludes with an invitation to the reader to think about the issues and take a particular action.

Subject Analysis

Writing Workshop

Average Student Model

Wham!

After soccer practice, you leave school and are late for work. It's rush hour. You are in a hurry. There's an auto accident in the next lane, which other cars are going past slowly. You can't resist, either. When you come close to the accident, you look out the window and see paramedics working over an unconscious woman. You wonder if she's dead or maybe in shock. Maybe, if you had gotten here earlier, that would be you lying on the ground. Still looking, still wondering, you hear a loud crash. You've just run into the car in front of you. Fortunately, neither you nor the other driver is hurt, but imagine what might have happened if you had been traveling at 60, 70, even 80 miles an hour!

We spend so much time in cars that we forget we are traveling in enormous, heavy hunks of steel, side by side with others, often moving at very fast speeds and often under adverse conditions, such as bad weather, bad road conditions, distraction or physical impairment, or poor automotive maintenance. Here are some suggestions for changing our driving habits.

First, slow down, and put some space between you and other cars. There should be one car's length for every ten miles per hour of speed between automobiles. There should be more distance at night and in bad weather. Pay attention to the posted speed limits, but go with the flow of traffic. If everyone around you is going well over the speed limit, increase your speed, too.

Don't drink and drive, and stay alert. More than half of all accidents are caused by drunk drivers. Also, be careful about taking certain medications that might have the effect of making you drowsy. Never get in a car with an impaired driver. Be cautious, too, for <u>signs of impairment in other cars</u> on the road, such as erratic driving. Always put your seat belt on, no matter whether you are a driver or a passenger, and check to be sure it is working all right.

Bad road conditions cause many accidents. If you are approaching a construction site, slow down and keep your eyes open for heavy equipment, and for signalers, or obstructions in the road. No matter where or when you are

1. Exclamatory title is intriguing.

2. The writer introduces the analysis with an interesting example but needs to combine sentences and use more varied sentence structures.

3. Identifies the main idea or thesis of the analysis.

4. Identifies the first part of the analysis and adds supporting details.

5. Word *cars* should be changed to *drivers* for clarity, since the cars themselves are not responsible for erratic driving.

For use with Pupil's Edition pp. 410–415

Subject Analysis

Average Student Model *continued*

driving, remember thinking ahead and be ready to stop or take evasive action at a moment's notice. This means to always keep your eyes on the road and checking the rearview mirror frequently. Look for other vehicles, for bicycles, and for children in the road. Slow down at intersections, even if the light is green. Another driver might be coming along the other way and just go straight through the red light.

Make sure that the vehicle you are driving is in tip-top shape. Check the engine, brakes, lights, and tires frequently. Wash your windows so that you have clear visibility all around. To drive and listening to music is a lot of fun, but at times it can be hazardous. Loud music may prevent you from hearing sirens or honking horns warning you of danger. You may get so caught up in listening to the music and singing along and even tapping your foot that you forget you are steering a two-ton killer at top speeds. Changing a tape or radio station may distract your attention from the road.

Some people are better drivers than others. Most people are merely adequate drivers, and many are downright incompetent. People do the strangest things in cars. They eat, they shave, they light cigarettes, they read maps, they talk on the phone, they address envelopes or scribble notes to themselves, they comb their hair, they put on makeup and lipstick, they adjust their mirrors and their seats, they keep up running conversations with people riding in the back seats. They don't signal or brake. They change lanes without looking. They run stop signs and red lights and race madly through school zones. Watch out for them!

Defensive driving courses are offered in most cities. You can look in the phone book or call up the automobile club to find out where they are in your city. It's a good idea to learn as much as possible about safe driving, so be sure to take one of those courses.

6. Identifies additional components of the analysis and provides examples. However, failure to use parallel structure disrupts the flow of ideas.

7. Combines two topics in one paragraph without using transitional words or phrases.

8. Verbs are not parallel in structure.

9. Includes too much detail; also, lacks conjunction *and* before last item in series.

10. Conclusion suggests an action the reader might take, but it could include more information and end on a stronger note.

Subject Analysis

Writing Workshop

Weak Student Model

Dangerous Driving Habits

We spend so much time in cars that we forget we are traveling in hunks of steel, next to others, often moving at very fast speeds and often under adverse conditions, such as bad weather. <u>Or bad road conditions</u>, distraction or physical impairment, or poor automotive maintenance. We need to change our driving habits.

You leave school. You are late for work. Soccer practice is over. It's rush hour. You are in a hurry. There's an accident in the next lane, which other cars are going past. They're going past slowly. You can't resist, either. When you come to the accident, you <u>look</u> out the window and <u>seeing</u> paramedics. There is an unconscious woman. You wonder, is she dead or maybe in shock. Maybe, if you had gotten here <u>more earlier</u>, that would be you. Maybe you would be in an accident. Then you hear a loud crash. You've just run into the car in front of you. You were traveling slowly so nobody was hurt. But if you had been going <u>more faster</u>, maybe at 60, 70, and even 80 miles an hour, you or somebody else might have been really badly hurt.

Slow down, and put some space between you and other cars. There should be one car's length between automobiles for every ten miles per hour. There should be more distance at night and in bad weather. Pay attention to what the signs say that the speed limits are, but don't be the only one going slow. If everyone around you is going really, really fast, you should go really fast, too. Otherwise, someone might just come up behind you and hit you.

Don't drink and drive. Stay alert. A bunch of accidents happen when drunk drivers get out there on the road. <u>Also, some medications that might have the effect of making you drowsy</u>. Never get in a car with somebody who can't drive very well. And look out for signs of other drivers who can't drive very well in other cars on the road. Always put your seat belt on, no matter whether you are a driver or a passenger. It could save your life. Look at it every now and then to be sure it is working, too.

1. Opens with a weak paragraph. Another Option:
• Begin with the second paragraph, which provides a real-life example.

2. Should avoid beginning sentences with *or, and,* or *but;* should use complete sentences.

3. Should use parallel constructions to express ideas that are parallel in meaning.

4. Uses double comparisons.

5. Does not identify main idea of analysis or indicate that this is the first supporting idea.

6. Sentence fragment should be revised to make it a complete sentence.

For use with Pupil's Edition pp. 410–415

CHAPTER 20

Subject Analysis

Weak Student Model *continued*

Construction sites cause a lot of accidents. Bad road conditions cause a lot of accidents. When you are coming to a construction site, slow down and keep your eyes open for heavy equipment, and also for signalers, or things in the road. No matter where or when you are driving, remember to think ahead and be ready to stop or take evasive action really fast. This means to always keep your eyes on the road, and to check the rearview mirror frequently. Look for other vehicles, bicycles, and children in the road. Slow down at intersections so you can stop if you have to. You might even watch out for other drivers going the other way who don't stop. This is another good reason for slowing down at intersections.

7. Does not use transitional words or phrases to introduce additional ideas that support the main idea.

Check the engine, brakes, lights, and tires a lot. Wash your windows. This way you can actually see out of them. The car should be in really good shape. To drive and listening to music is a lot of fun, but sometimes it can get you into an accident. Loud music may cover up the sounds of sirens or honking horns. You might be humming along or singing out loud, or just enjoying the music, and forget where you are or what you are doing. Changing a tape or radio station makes you look away from the road, and that can spell disaster. It is easy to forget you are steering a heavy machine and going really fast.

Most people are just okay drivers. Some people are incompetent drivers. Some people are better drivers. People do the strangest things, like eating, they shave, light cigarettes, they read maps, talk on the phone, they address envelopes or scribble notes to themselves, comb their hair, put on makeup and lipstick, they adjust their mirrors and their seats, and they keep up running conversations with people riding in the back seats. They don't signal or put their foot on the brake. They change lanes without looking to see who is already there. They run stop signs and red lights and go fast through school zones. Better be careful!

8. Does not use parallel constructions; includes too many details.

Look in your phone book for a defensive driving course and sign up for it.

9. The writer ends with a weak conclusion.

Subject Analysis

Writing Workshop

Rubric for Evaluation

Ideas and Content	Weak	Average	Strong
1. Introduces the subject in an interesting, informative manner			
2. Identifies the parts that compose the subject			
3. Examines and explains each part			
4. Shows how the parts relate to the whole subject and support the main idea or thesis			

Structure and Form			
5. Presents information in a logical order			
6. Includes an effective introduction, body, and conclusion			

Grammar, Usage, and Mechanics			
7. Contains no more than two or three minor errors in spelling, capitalization, and punctuation			
8. Contains no more than two or three minor errors in grammar and usage			

Writing Progress to Date (Writing Portfolio)

The strongest aspect of this writing is _____

_____

The final version shows improvement over the rough draft in this way: _____

_____

A specific improvement over past assignments in your portfolio is _____

_____

A skill to work on in future assignments is _____

_____

Additional comments: _____

_____

For use with Pupil's Edition pp. 410–415

CHAPTER 20

Business Writing

Writing Workshop

Prewriting

When you have decided what kind of position you want, use the chart below to list the qualifications you have that relate to the job. First, write in the left-hand column all of the activities, education, and experience from your past that you think are important. Then select the items that seem most pertinent and use the right-hand column to categorize these merits and to list them in order of importance.

Job Objective:	
List of Qualifications	**Most Relevant and Important Qualifications**
	Experience: _____
	1.
	2.
	3.
	4.
	5.
	Education and Honors: _____
	1.
	2.
	3.
	4.
	5.
	Activities and Interests: _____
	1.
	2.
	3.
	4.
	5.

CHAPTER 21

Business Writing

Drafting and Elaboration

The selection below is from the first draft of a résumé for a position as a radio deejay. Use the Suggestions for Elaboration, the information from the Reader's Notebook, and your own ideas to develop the draft so that it is more specific and complete. Write your draft on a separate sheet of paper.

Draft

Kathleen Reslet
3406 Green Street
Ellingsworth, IL 60606
(773) 555-4567

Job Objective
Radio deejay

Experience

- Worked on high school radio station
- Interned at local radio station
- Sing in a band

Education and Honors

- High school graduate
- Radio/Communication class at community college

Activities and Interests

- A/V Club
- Drama Club
- Deejay at friends' parties

Suggestions for Elaboration

- Give specific names of schools, businesses, and organizations.
- Tell more about the band and the applicant's participation in it.
- Give the year in which the applicant graduated from high school.
- Specify what positions the applicant held in the clubs listed.

READER'S NOTEBOOK

■ The applicant worked as a deejay for Elston High School's radio station, WEHS. ■ She was also an intern for WJAZ, her town's local jazz station.

■ Kathleen and her friends formed a jazz and blues band called Low Notes.

■ Low Notes performs on weekends at coffee houses, and Kathleen is the lead singer. ■ During her last semester at Elston in the year 2000, she took a class in Radio and Communication at Ellingsworth Community College. ■ Kathleen was president of the Audio/Visual Club and was a member and an actor in the Drama Club in high school.

For use with Pupil's Edition pp. 418–425

Business Writing

Peer Response Guide

It may be difficult to know how clear and effective your résumé is. To find out if you have achieved the desired outcome, ask a peer reviewer to read your résumé and answer the following questions:

1. What is my job objective?

Response:

Suggestions for Revision:

2. What information could I include to make my résumé more complete?

Response:

Suggestions for Revision:

3. What information do you find most useful and pertinent to the job I am applying for?

Response:

Suggestions for Revision:

Business Writing

Peer Response Guide *continued*

4. What information do you find least useful?

Response:

Suggestions for Revision:

5. Would you reorder any of the items that I listed? If so, how?

Response:

Suggestions for Revision:

6. If you were a potential employer, what overall impression would you have of me?

Response:

Suggestions for Revision:

For use with Pupil's Edition pp. 418–425

Business Writing

Revising, Editing, and Proofreading

Revising

TARGET SKILL ➤ Avoiding Wordiness

When revising your résumé, ask yourself the following questions:

• Have I delivered my message quickly, strongly, and without unnecessary words?

• Have I stated my name, address, telephone number, and job objective?

• Have I listed my educational background?

• Have I presented details about my work experience, skills, and interests?

Editing and Proofreading

TARGET SKILL ➤ Checking Punctuation and Spelling

Refer to the bulleted list below to edit this section from a first draft of a résumé for a position as a radio deejay. Use proofreading marks to correct errors in grammar, usage, mechanics, and spelling. Copy your corrected draft on a separate sheet of paper.

• Make sure that there are absolutely no errors in punctuation, capitalization, grammar, or spelling.

• Replace vague terms with more specific ones.

• Check to be sure that the format is consistent.

• Eliminate unnecessary words and phrases.

Draft

Job Objective

Radio station worker, full-time

Education and Honor's

• Graduated and got a diploma from Elston high school in the year 2000.

• Ellingsworth Community College, Radio/Comunication class in 2000

Activities and Interests

• Audio/Vissual Club, president

• Drama Club. Member

• Deejay, at friends' parties and other places

Applying

Now edit and proofread your own résumé. Refer to the bulleted list above.

Résumé

Strong Student Model

David Clementi
130 Kensington Street
Hugo, Oklahoma 74743
(580) 555-0032
e-mail dclem1@aol.com

Job Objective: Full-time employment as an occupational therapist's aide

Experience
School Year 2000

• *Volunteer at Helping Hand Nursing Home in Grant, OK.* After-school. Assisted residents during physical therapy <u>(PT) sessions</u>, spent time with them — reading, playing games, talking. <u>Was frequently complimented by staff and residents for my cheerfulness and patience.</u>

Summer 1999 and 2000

• *Assistant caregiver at Kids Count Day Care in Hugo, OK.* Full-time. In charge of a group of 4-year-olds: reading to them, feeding them, playing games, <u>treating them for occasional minor injuries</u>.

School Year 1998 and 1999

• *Aide at Children's Hospital in Hugo, OK.* After-school. Transported patients to and from <u>PT sessions</u>, read to them, ran errands for staff.

Education and Achievements

• Harrison High School, Class of 2000
• Honor Roll
• <u>Award for Most Improvement in Sign Language AMSLAN</u>
• <u>Helping Hand Prize, awarded by residents to the volunteer with the best attitude</u>

Activities and Interests

• Sign Language Club, vice-president
• Fitness Club, member
• American Red Cross, volunteer

References Available on request

1. Résumé is attractive, information is clearly presented, and applicant's qualifications are evident.

2. Personal data is complete.

3. Objective is specific, clear, and reasonable.

4. Writer emphasizes experience, listing jobs in the appropriate order. Another option:
• Give primary emphasis to skills (working with children and senior citizens).

5. Entries are complete yet succinct. Writer uses action verbs.

6. Mentions a character trait that bears on his value as an employee.

7. Includes awards that would be of interest to a prospective employer, along with educational data.

8. Lists activities relevant to job goal.

9. Includes a notation about references.

Résumé

Average Student Model

David Clementi
130 Kensington Street
Hugo, Oklahoma
(580) 555-0032
e-mail dclem1@aol.com

Job Objective
• Full-time work in occupational therapy

Skills
Child Care

• Kids Count Day Care in Hugo, OK. For two summers, I took care of four-year-olds in the following ways: reading stories to them, making lunch and snacks for them, playing games with them.

• Children's Hospital in Hugo, OK. For two years after school, I helped kids get to and from physical therapy sessions. I also read to them. I ran errands for the nursing staff: transporting specimens, delivering flowers and mail to patients, picking up and delivering medical records.

Senior-Citizen Care

• Helping Hand Nursing Home in Grant, OK. For one year, I volanteered after school, assisting residence as needed during physical therapy sessions. I also spent time with them doing the following: reading to them, play games with them, or just talk. I was often complimented by the staff and by residents.

Education and Awards
Harrison High School, Class of 2000
Honor Roll
AMSLAN Award
Helping Hand Prize

Activities and Interests
Sign Language Club, vice-president
Fitness Club, member
American Red Cross, volunteer

References
Available on request

1. Generally well laid out and organized, although bulleted lists are not maintained throughout.

2. Personal data is essentially complete, though ZIP code is missing.

3. Objective should be more specific and reasonable. The writer's credentials do not qualify him for work as a physical therapist, although they do qualify him for an aide's job.

4. The writer has chosen to emphasize skills, an appropriate choice.
Another Option:
• Give primary emphasis to experience.

5. Entries convey essential information and employ action verbs, but they are a bit wordy.

6. Errors in spelling and grammar indicate that proofreading was not complete.

7. The writer should be clearer about the nature of the compliments and awards.

8. Activities and interests relate to the job goal.

9. References have been mentioned.

Résumé

Weak Student Model

CHAPTER 21

David Clementi
130 Kensington Street
Hugo, Oklahoma
555–0032
e-mail dclem1@aol.com

Job Objective: *Full-time therapist*

Experiences: *Kids Count Day Care, 2 years (group of 4 year olds). Childrens' hospitil, 2 years (transported kids, errends). Helping Hand Nurseing Home, 1 year (volunteer). Was complemented by residence and staff about my being patient and that I am cheerfull.*

Education: *Harrison High School, Class of 2000 Honor Roll*

Achievements and Awards: *AMSLAN Award Helping Hand Prize*

Activities and Interests: *archery canoeing hiking*

1. Résumé looks slight. Organization does not emphasize the writer's special skills and abilities. Type is hard to read.

2. Personal data is missing: The ZIP code and the area code have been omitted.

3. The job objective is too vague.

4. Experience and skills are poorly presented. Job descriptions are not nearly detailed enough.

5. Errors in spelling, punctuation, and grammar indicate poor proofreading.

6. This entry, meant to stress the applicant's character, is unclear (to which job does it refer?) and poorly written.

7. Listings are incomplete. What were the awards for?

8. This information is not likely to be of interest to an employer.

9. No mention is made of references.

For use with Pupil's Edition pp. 418–425

Procedural Narrative

Strong Student Model

Manual for Student Safety Monitors:
Emergency Exits

All teachers, staff, and student safety monitors must be familiar with the procedure to follow during an emergency exit for a fire drill or bomb threat. This section explains the responsibilities of the student safety monitor during an emergency exit for a fire drill or a bomb threat and outlines the procedure that must be followed.

Responsibilities

- You must attend a training session on emergency exits, run by the assistant principal, the day before school opens.

- You are responsible for lining students up, following behind to make sure the group stays together (out of and back into the building), and helping maintain student silence during the emergency exit.

- You must make sure that fire drill procedures and fire exits are posted in your classroom at all times.

Fire Drill Procedure

1. <u>After</u> the principal has announced that there is to be a drill, the fire alarm will sound. <u>At this time</u>, help students line up <u>while</u> your teacher retrieves the daily attendance sheet.

2. As your teacher leads your class to the designated safe spot (the corner of Highland and Cottage), follow your class and make sure that everyone stays together.

3. <u>Remember</u> to maintain student silence throughout the drill.

4. Once your class is at the safe spot, your teacher uses the daily attendance sheet to make sure that all class members are present. Check to make sure the proper students are responding as their names are called.

5. When the all-clear signal sounds, <u>follow</u> your class as your teacher leads them back to the classroom.

Bomb Threat Procedure

1. The principal announces a fire drill and then says, "Leave doors and windows open." This is the signal that the school has received a bomb threat.

2. Help the teacher make sure of the following:
   - The windows and doors are open.
   - The lights are not touched. (Don't turn them on or off.)
   - Electrical power sources aren't touched. (Don't turn on or off.)

3. The rest of the procedure is identical to the fire-drill procedure, as outlined above.

1. The audience, purpose, and topic of the procedure is clearly stated.

2. When a sequence is being described, numbers indicate the order of the steps.

3. Consistently clear about who does what, when, and where.

4. Signal words are used to cue proper sequence (*after, at this time, while*).

5. Each step is succinctly stated but detailed enough to make the task clear.

6. States the specific time frame for a particular task when such information is needed.

7. Relies on the active voice throughout, using imperatives to explain tasks to the intended audience.

8. Is particularly explicit about important safety measures.

CHAPTER 21

Procedural Narrative

Average Student Model

Student Safety Monitor Manual: Emergency Exits

A major role of the student safety monitor is to assist teachers during emergency exits (fire drills and bomb threats).

As safety monitor, you will learn about emergency exit procedures at a special training session the day before school starts. At this time, you will learn your responsibilities: lining up students for the drill, following behind as your class goes outside, keeping everyone quiet, and making sure fire drill procedures and fire exits are posted in your classroom. Below is the exact procedure to follow, listed in order, for fire drills and bomb threats.

Fire Drill Procedure

- The principle announces that there is a fire drill. The alarm sounds.
- Line up the students in your classroom. Your teacher will be making sure she has the daily attendence sheet.
- Follow your class as your teacher leads them outside.
- It is important for you to make sure everyone stays quiet throughout the drill.
- The class proceeds to the designated safe spot (the corner of Highland and Cottage). Your teacher uses the attendance sheet to make sure everyone is present. You should help him or her.
- The all-clear signal comes on. Follow your class as your teacher leads everyone back to the classroom.

Bomb Threat Procedure

This procedure is exactly the same as the fire drill except for these two things:

- The principle announces there is a fire drill. She ends by saying, "Leave doors and windows open." This means it is really a bomb threat, so you should do the next set of steps.
- Help the teacher make sure the doors and windows are left open.
- Leave the lights alone.
- Leave anything else electrical alone.

1. States the topic and audience. Has included the purpose as well, but not until the end of the next paragraph.

2. Includes essential information, although text could be organized more clearly, using a heading and/or bullets.

3. The exact sequence—who does what, when—could be more precise. Addition of signal words *(before, after, at the same time)* would help clarify sequence.

4. Minor spelling and grammar errors indicate that proofreading was not complete.

5. There are occasional shifts in voice.

6. Should specify how the monitor helps the teacher. Should make the hierarchy of steps in the second procedure clearer—the first bulleted step should not introduce the other bulleted steps.

7. Because this information is important, the writer should highlight the text in some way—by using boldfaced type or by adding a DO or DON'T statement.

For use with Pupil's Edition pp. 418–425

Procedural Narrative

Weak Student Model

Fire Drills and Bomb Threats

Being a safety monitor is an important responsibility. You have to know what to do. This is why you have to go to a training session the day before school and learn about emergency exits.

Steps to follow:

1. <u>You have to</u> line up students in a fire drill. The teacher <u>has get</u> the <u>attendence</u> sheet.

2. The teacher leads the class outside and <u>you follow</u> behind. <u>Your making sure everyone quite.</u>

3. Your teacher makes sure everyone is present. You have to help.

4. Your <u>disegnated</u> safe spot is the corner of Highland, which is at least 500 feet from the school. <u>This is why its safe.</u>

5. When it's over, follow as your class goes back.

6. If there is a bomb threat, not a drill, the principal says, "Leave doors and windows open." Then you and the teacher know it's a bomb threat. So you have to make sure doors and windows ARE open.

7. Also in a bomb threat, don't touch lights or other electrical things. Leave them as they are. Don't turn them on or off.

1. Introductory remarks are not necessary to the procedural narrative.

2. Opening paragraph needs to be rewritten to clearly state topic and purpose. Title should be more specific.

3. Information is poorly organized. The procedure for a bomb threat, for example, has been tacked on to the end of the fire drill rather than being set up as its own procedure.

4. Voice shifts frequently, adding to the overall lack of clarity.

5. Numerous errors in spelling and grammar indicate a poor job of proofreading.

6. Writer needs to be clear about exactly what gets done, who does it, when, and whether particular materials are needed.

CHAPTER 21

Summary

Strong Student Model

Writing Workshop
*These writing models are also
available in **Assessment Masters**.*

CHAPTER 21

Summary: **"The Job Hunter's Guide to the Internet"**
by Sy Burnaught (www.burnaught.com/jobs2000)
Date: **October 6, 2001**
To: **Job-Hunting Students Who Can Go Online**

1. Identifies source and is specific about audience.

The Internet is huge and keeps expanding. Online job hunters need to know "what to look for and what to look out for." The author arranges information and advice in three sections.

2. Briefly states the purpose of the original article. Uses the section heads to express main ideas. Another Option:
• State main ideas of article in paragraph form.

Knowing the Net

The "Net is always open," if you have the equipment to go—and stay—online. No print article can stay current on the Net, so the author provides the URL to his Web site, which is updated weekly.

What to Look For: Net Promises

The Internet can provide these job-hunting services:

3. Summary is clearly organized and succinct, picking up on section heads and using a bulleted format.

Another Option:
• Arrange the information by category (résumé postings, job listings, job contacts, job research) in a numbered list.

- *Gets your résumé seen by the widest range of employers.* There are sites devoted to résumé postings in various fields.

- *Provides current job listings from all over the country and the world.* You don't have to find newspapers from everywhere or make expensive calls to see what jobs are available.

- *Enables you to make job-hunting contacts:* direct contact with people who can help you get interviews, potential employers, other people in your field (for advice) and career counselors.

- *Helps you research careers, companies, and job locations.* The Internet is a vast source of information. Search engines—such as Alta Vista, Lycos, and Yahoo (which has a directory to search engines)—sort through and help you find specific information.

4. Sticks to essential information.

5. Includes explanations and pertinent information so the summary can be read independently of the original.

What to Look Out For: Net Reality

Job hunters on the Internet need to be realistic and cautious:

6. Includes recommendations and reasons for the recommendations from the article.

- *Résumé postings.* Most employers use the Internet as a last resort, if at all, and have thousands of résumés to review. If you do post yours, remember that *anybody* can read it. Include an e-mail address or phone number so that an employer can contact you, but don't include any addresses.

- *Job listings.* Be specific in your searches (career, position, job location). There are 11,000+ job sites and no central listing.

- *Job contacts.* The Internet is excellent as a source of contacts. Remember to be polite and to follow through on a contact.

- *Job research.* It is easy to get sidetracked online. As the author says, "There are so many sites to see!" You can spend a whole day supposedly job-hunting and have nothing to show for it. Stay focused and make each site count.

7. Uses quotation marks to set off original wording from paraphrasing.

8. Summary is about one-tenth of the original 10-page article.

For use with Pupil's Edition pp. 418–425

Summary

Average Student Model

Summary: "The Job Hunter's Guide to the Internet"
by Sy Burnaught
Date: October 6, 2001
To: Students Who Want Jobs

The author of this article wants to help students use the Internet to find jobs. The article begins with some information about the Internet, which is huge and always changing. <u>Nobody really knows how many people go online to look for jobs, but the number does seem to be growing</u>. For the most current information about jobs, you should use the author's website, which he updates every week (www.burnaught.com/jobs2000).

The article covers four areas of job-hunting that you can do on the Internet. The author provides information (What to Look For) and advice (What to Look Out For).

1. **Résumé Postings** If you put your résumé on the Internet, alot of people will see it. There are sights just for résumés, usually in specific fields. Just be careful and dont put your own address or any business addresses on your résumé. But do include an e-mail address or phone number so that an actual employer is able to contact you.

2. **Job Listings** Without buying a newspaper or making a phone call, you can see job openings from all over the country and from all over the world. Unfortunately, the author points out, there is no central place for these listings. In fact, there are over 11,000 job sites to visit, so you will be kept very busy.

3. **Job Contacts** You can make direct contact on the Internet with various kinds of people who can help you: people who can get you interviews, employers looking to hire people for jobs, people in the same field as you who can give you advice, and career counselors who can help you decide on a career that works for you and then tell you what you need to do to get into that career.

4. **Job Research/Information** The Internet is a great source of job information. You need to use a search engine, like Alta Vista or Lycos or Yahoo, to help you sort through all this information and find sites that will be useful to you. Find out about careers and job training. Find out about particular companies. Learn what it's like to live in different locations. Just remember that it's easy to get sidetracked on the Internet and bounce from site to site. You have to stay focused on what you are doing.

1. Identifies source and audience, although could be more specific about the audience.

2. Doesn't entirely capture the author's main point—job-hunters need to be aware of shortcomings and potential problems to negotiate the Net.

3. The underlined sentence is not critical and could be deleted.

4. Summary uses the four job-hunting areas covered to organize the information.
Another Option:
• Use the author's own section headings as subheads.

5. Has minor grammatical and spelling errors.

6. The author's recommendation is given but not his reason for giving it.

7. Language is sometimes a bit wordy.

8. Summary is about one-tenth the length of the original article.

CHAPTER 21

Summary

Weak Student Model

Summary: "The Job Hunter's Guide to the Internet"
Date: October 6, 2001
To: Students

There are three sections in this article about the Internet:

- Knowing the Net
- What to Look For: Net Promises
- What to Look Out For: Net Reality

The Internet is the biggest source of information in the world. It is always changing, so the author can't keep up with it. His Web site gets updated every week, so you should visit there.

Here's are some things you should know about the Internet:

1. If you put your resume on the Internet, alot of people will see them. Employers may see it and be interested. But others too. So don't put your address on the resume. Just a phone number.
2. You can find job listings for jobs all over the world.
3. There are no central job listing. In stead, you could say there are so many sites to see (about 11,000 or more!).
4. You can contact people who can help—employers, people in the field you want to be in, career counselors.
5. Be polite when you contact people. Always thank them for helping you. You can ask advice of people in your field. Ask them if they like their job or what you can do to get into their field.
6. You can use the Net to do research on different careers and the training you need.
7. You can find out about certain companies and where they are located. Also, you can find out what it's like to live there.
8. When you search the Internet, which is huge, use a search engine to help you find things. Some search engines are Alta Vista, Lycos, and Yahoo.

1. Author's name is missing. Audience should be more specific.

2. Identifies the main ideas of the essay by listing its sections but neglects to convey its overall purpose.

3. Important information is missing. What, for example, is the URL for the author's Web site?

4. Summary jumps around instead of reflecting the structure of the original article. Other Options:
- Use the author's section headings as subheads.
- Use the categories covered (résumé postings, job listings, job contacts, job research) to organize the information.

5. Numerous spelling and grammatical errors indicate a poor job of proofreading.

6. Information is often confusing and incomplete.

7. Has directly quoted the author without properly indicating this fact.

8. Summary's shortness indicates a lack of detail.

For use with Pupil's Edition pp. 418–425

CHAPTER 21

Business Writing

Writing Workshop

Rubric for Evaluation

Ideas and Content	Weak	Average	Strong
1. States the writer's name, address, and telephone number			
2. Gives a clear statement of the writer's employment objective			
3. Presents details about the writer's experience or skills			
4. Lists educational background			
5. Provides information about special skills and activities			

Structure and Form			
6. Presents the writer's abilities in a positive light			
7. Is well organized, attractive, and correct			

Grammar, Usage, and Mechanics			
8. Contains no more than two or three minor errors in spelling, capitalization, and punctuation			
9. Contains no more than two or three minor errors in grammar and usage			

CHAPTER 21

Writing Progress to Date (Writing Portfolio)

The strongest aspect of this writing is _____

_____

The final version shows improvement over the rough draft in this way: _____

_____

A specific improvement over past assignments in your portfolio is_____

_____

A skill to work on in future assignments is_____

_____

Additional comments: _____

_____

Proposal

Prewriting

A **proposal** is a document or speech that identifies a problem or need and offers a plan of action to solve the problem or meet the need. Your proposal may be about an issue affecting your family, school, or community. Alone or with friends, brainstorm problems or needs, or look for articles in the school or community newspaper. Interview friends and neighbors to find out what they see as problems or issues. Keep a list of all the problems and needs you identify. Next, choose one of them as a topic for your proposal. Then plan your proposal by answering the questions in the chart below.

Why is the issue important? How will my proposal meet the need (solve the problem)?
Who will be the audience for the proposal? What are their concerns? How can I persuade them to accept the proposal?
What steps are involved? What resources are needed?
How hard will it be to carry out my plan? What are the arguments against the plan?
What information will I need to support the proposal? Where can I get the information?

For use with Pupil's Edition pp. 428–435

Proposal

Drafting and Elaboration

To write a truly persuasive proposal, support your arguments with examples, statistics, quotations, or data from your own research. The paragraph below is from a draft of a proposal for a visiting writers program for high school students. Make the proposal more persuasive by following the Suggestions for Elaboration. Use information from the Reader's Notebook or add your own ideas. Write your elaborated paragraph on a separate sheet of paper.

Draft

Many students want to work on their writing skills. More students keep diaries or journals that they're not required to keep, and more are also writing stories and poems on their own. Also, students who do more than one draft tend to be more proficient in writing than students who do not.

Suggestions for Elaboration

- Provide statistics to support the claim that more students are writing outside of class.
- Add further information about practices that can improve writing.
- Explain how you think such practices contribute to better writing.
- Identify sources for your claims and statistics, and note the specific grade levels covered.

CHAPTER 22

READER'S NOTEBOOK

■ About 33 percent of eleventh graders keep a diary or journal outside of class (National Center for Education Statistics). ■ Eighteen percent of eleventh graders write stories or poems outside of class (same study).

■ These percentages have increased since 1984. ■ Twelfth graders who make lists or outlines and who complete more than one draft tend to write more proficiently than students who do not (National Assessment of Educational Progress). ■ Outlining keeps writers from getting off the subject; revising helps them recognize mistakes.

Proposal

Peer Response Guide

A proposal can be persuasive only if the writer has communicated her or his ideas clearly to the reader. To help you evaluate the clarity of your proposal and the strength of the facts and arguments you have used to support it, ask a classmate to read your proposal and answer these questions.

1. What problem or need did I outline?

Response:

Suggestions for Revision:

2. What other points should I add to support my plan?

Response:

Suggestions for Revision:

3. What parts of my proposal needed more detail or explanation?

Response:

Suggestions for Revision:

For use with Pupil's Edition pp. 428–435

Proposal

Peer Response Guide *continued*

4. How did I address opponents to my plan?

   Response:

   Suggestions for Revision:

5. What can I add to my proposal to decrease opposition to my plan?

   Response:

   Suggestions for Revision:

6. Who is likely to oppose my plan and why?

   Response:

   Suggestions for Revision:

Proposal

Revising, Editing, and Proofreading

Revising

TARGET SKILL ➤ Achieving Clarity

As you revise your proposal, ask yourself the following questions:

- Have I used specific words and phrases to make my meaning clear?
- Have I targeted a specific audience?
- Have I clearly defined a problem or stated a need?
- Have I presented a clear solution and used evidence to demonstrate that the plan is workable?

Editing and Proofreading

TARGET SKILL ➤ Correcting Fragments

Use the suggestions below to revise the following paragraph from a draft of a proposal for a visiting writers program. Use proofreading marks to correct errors in grammar, usage, mechanics, and spelling.

- Correct sentence fragments so that they express complete thoughts.
- Rephrase sentences to eliminate unnecessary words.
- Replace informal words and phrases with clearer, more formal ones.
- Clarify antecedents of pronouns.

> **Draft**
>
> Organizing a writers program that allows each student to come into contact with the writers who would be happy to visit taft High School during the time the program is being held is a very good idea. Such a cool thing for the students! We could do the program throughout the whole school. The writers would stop by several diffrent English classes and do their writing workshops. Followed by a short question and answer period. Students could ask them their questions and they could answer them.

Applying

Now edit your own proposal. Refer to the bulleted list above.

For use with Pupil's Edition pp. 428–435

Proposal

Strong Student Model

Writing Workshop
These writing models are also
available in Assessment Masters.

A Proposal to Organize a Visiting Writers Program at Taft High School

Summary

The following proposal requests approval for and support from the administration and faculty of Taft High School for organizing a visiting writers program. The program will increase the understanding and appreciation of Taft students for the value of writing skills by allowing them to interact with professional writers from a number of fields, including journalism, fiction, poetry, and essay writing.

1. Clearly states the purpose of the proposal and addresses the audience.

Need

Understanding how professional writers work is important because it helps students broaden their own writing skills. According to the National Center for Education Statistics, 32.9 percent of eleventh-grade students keep diaries or journals outside of class, while 18 percent write stories or poems outside of class. Both of these statistics represent increases since 1984. Additionally, according to the National Assessment of Educational Progress, twelfth-grade students who do prewriting activities (such as making lists or outlines) and who do more than one draft of a paper tend to be more proficient in writing than students who do not engage in these activities.

2. The writer uses facts and statistics to show the importance of the issue.
Other Options:
• Provide an example or anecdote.
• Use expert testimony.

My random poll of 30 senior students at Taft shows that 60 percent of students do not feel they are good writers, despite doing regular writing assignments in class. Some of these students state that, while writing is hard for them, they do not think they will need writing skills in the future. Other comments include, "As long as the teachers tell me exactly what to write, I'm fine," and "I don't plan on being a writer, so why do I need to know how to write?" The poll clearly shows the need for the school to develop a plan that will give all students at least a basic understanding of the value of writing skills.

3. Identifies problem and supports it with data from poll.

4. Sums up the need.

To solve this problem, members of the faculty have suggested that students do more writing through a variety of elective courses, including writing workshops. This is a good idea. However, it will take time and a reorganization of the English curriculum. Classes will have to be developed to give each student exposure to different forms of writing, including newspaper and

5. Thoughtfully addresses an alternative idea.

Proposal

Strong Student Model *continued*

magazine writing, short story writing, and personal essay writing. Although this reorganization of the curriculum is a good long-term solution, students would benefit in the short term from listening to professional writers share their experiences in the worlds of writing and publishing.

Proposed Solution

The solution is to organize a visiting writers program this fall. Such a program would allow each student to gain firsthand knowledge of writing by inviting six to eight professional writers who live throughout the state to visit Taft High School. During the week-long program, writers would speak to individual English classes in different grades and lead writing workshops in their areas of expertise. The writers would also participate in panel discussions on different aspects of writing and give readings from their works in front of the entire school. These events would be free and open to the public.

To implement this plan would require commitment from the whole school. The English department faculty would need to invite the writers and to plan what classroom and panel discussion topics would be most beneficial for students. Student volunteers would need to do much of the work in seeing that the program runs smoothly. The administration would need to deal with scheduling, and the maintenance and other staff would need to cope with the physical requirements of the program. Most of the costs, which would take the form of small honorariums paid to visiting writers, could probably come from the regular budgets of the administration and English department. Also, local businesses could donate materials or buy advertising on an events calendar.

A weeklong writers program would cut into the school-year calendar. However, many of the events would not have to disrupt the school day. Instead, they could be incorporated into existing school classes and functions. As a result, Taft High School students would gain a new appreciation and understanding of writing, and perhaps be motivated or inspired to build up their own writing skills.

6. Explains how plan would work. Idea that writers from "throughout the state" could come to the school for a small honorarium seems unrealistic.

7. The writer describes in general terms how to implement the plan. Other Options:
- Spell out steps needed to put plan into action.
- Identify people who back plan or are lined up to help.
- Give an estimate of the costs.

8. Addresses and refutes a possible objection.

For use with Pupil's Edition pp. 428–435

CHAPTER 22

Proposal

Writing Workshop

Average Student Model

A Proposal to Organize a Visiting Writers Program at Taft High School

Summary

The following is a request to the administration and faculty at Taft High School for a visiting writers program at Taft. This program will help Taft students learn to value writing skills by having them interact with a variety of writers.

1. States the purpose of the proposal and addresses the audience.

Need

Understanding what writers do helps students to make their own writing skills broader. According to the National Center for Education Statistics, more high school students are writing outside of class than ever before, and students do better when they plan their writing and do more than one draft. A random survey of 30 seniors revealed that 60% thought they were bad writers, even though they write a lot of English papers and do a lot of homework that involves writing. Some said that even though writing was the hardest thing they have to do in school, they're going to be computer software developers or get rich in business and they're not going to have to write in the future. As a couple of them put it, "My teachers tell me what to write, so it's no problem," and "I'm not going to be a writer, so I don't need to know how to write." In light of these comments, the school has to develop a plan that will give all students some kind of understanding of the value of writing.

2. Uses facts to show importance of the issue, but could be more specific. Other Options:
- Provide an example or anecdote.
- Use expert testimony.

3. Identifies problem and supports it with data from poll, but does not say where, when, or by whom poll was conducted.

4. Sums up the need.

Members of the English department have suggested that students do more writing to solve this problem. They suggest a variety of electives, including writing workshops. This is a good start. However, it will take some time and organizing to get these classes going. They will certainly be good classes, and they will help future students. But right now, students would really benefit from getting the chance to talk with real writers and ask them questions about writing and publishing.

5. Addresses alternative idea.

Proposed Solution

The solution then, is to organize a visiting writers program. This would allow each student to come in contact with six to eight professional writers who live nearby and would be willing to visit Taft High School

6. Explains how plan would work.

CHAPTER 22

Proposal

Average Student Model *continued*

during a specific week. It would be a school-wide event that everybody could participate in, as well as the faculty, staff, and people from the community. Writers would speak to different English classes and maybe lead writing workshops in their areas of expertise. These writers would also take part in panel discussions on different aspects of writing, and give readings from their work in front of the entire school. Everything would be free and open to the public.

To do all of this would require a major effort from the whole school. The English department would need to invite the writers and plan what they would like them to talk about in front of students. Students would need to do much of the planning and preparation for the writers' visits so that the program runs smoothly. The administration would need to make new schedules for that week, and the maintenance and other staff would need to make sure everything else is working. Most of the costs would be small. The administration might want to pay a small fee to each of the writers for agreeing to visit the school, but this could probably come from the school's regular budget for special events—and perhaps the English department could help as well. Also, a lot of local businesses could buy advertising on a calendar the school makes up for the week, or donate supplies.

A weeklong writers program would definitely cut into the regular school schedule. However, it is possible that many events could be incorporated into regular school classes and assemblies. The results would be very positive. Taft High School students would gain a new understanding of writing, and maybe try harder to improve their own writing skills. Both the school and the students would benefit.

7. Describes in general terms what is needed to implement the plan, but could be clearer.
Other Options:
- Spell out steps for putting plan into action.
- Identify people who back plan or are lined up to help.
- Give estimate of the costs.

8. Addresses and refutes a possible objection.

CHAPTER 22

For use with Pupil's Edition pp. 428–435

Proposal

Writing Workshop

Weak Student Model

A Proposal to Organize a Visiting Writers Program at Taft High School

Summary

This request is being made to the administration and faculty for a writers program at Taft High School. This program will enable students to learn about writing skills from actual writers who make their living writing and who come to visit the school and talk about everything they have learned in their writing.

1. Addresses the audience but does not clearly define the purpose of the proposal.

Need

Students' own writing skills will become better if they are able to learn from actual writers. No one doubts that most students can write their names or write an English paper, but not many of the students feel that they are good writers. Statistics show that more students than ever are writing stories and in journals they're not required to keep for a class, but some really dislike writing because it is very hard for them. Others think it is boring or that they will not need to do much writing when they are finished with school. A few people have said, "I am always being told by my teachers what to write for my assignment," and "I do not feel like paying attention to my writing more." As you can see, it is essential that the school do something to promote the value of writing to these and other students.

2. Does not use facts to support statements.

3. Uses quotations but does not clearly attribute them.

4. Vaguely sums up need for school to "do something."

Yes, students could take new and improved writing classes. This is a good first step to get students to write more and to explore the writing of short stories, poems, and other works. However, new classes do not happen overnight. It will be some time before these new classes are offered, and current students will have most likely graduated by then without improving their writing at all. Therefore, students in school now would benefit the most from the above proposal being accepted and then being undertaken during the current school year.

5. Addresses alternative idea.

Proposed Solution

Organizing a writers program that allows each student to come in contact with actual writers is a very good idea. The writers program would be held throughout the school and everybody, including teachers, principals, and staff, would have the chance to take part in it. The writers would stop by different English classes and do

6. Explains in overly general terms how plan would work.

Proposal

Weak Student Model *continued*

writing workshops with the classes in the formats that they write in. Students could ask them questions, and <u>they</u> could answer <u>them</u>. <u>They</u> could also have a discussion with the school as a group on different aspects of writing and give readings from their works in front of the whole school. It would all be free and the public could be invited, too.

7. Pronoun antecedents are not clear.

The English department would need to invite the writers and plan what <u>they</u> would like <u>them</u> to do with the students. Students would have to help out too, by doing much of the planning and preparation for the writers' visits. If the administration would be willing to make new schedules and maintenance would be willing to clean up afterward, the writers' program would most likely run very smoothly and be a great success. Even better, if <u>they</u> could pay the writers a small amount of money, more writers might be willing to visit the school. Also, a lot of local businesses could help out by sponsoring the writers' program and get free advertising for themselves.

8. Does not clearly spell out steps, people, or costs involved; does not address possible objections.

This program is definitely needed and would make the idea of writing far more interesting for students in the present and in the future. If students see living and breathing writers who care about what they write, they may like writing more, or want to become writers themselves in the future. Either way, they would gain a new understanding of writers and writing that could only benefit them in the long run. That is what students are supposed to learn in high school, things that can help them after they get out.

9. Closing sentence is weak.

For use with Pupil's Edition pp. 428–435

Proposal

Rubric for Evaluation

Ideas and Content	Weak	Average	Strong
1. Targets a specific audience			
2. Clearly defines a problem or states a need			
3. Presents a clear solution			
4. Uses evidence to demonstrate that the plan is workable			
5. Shows how the plan will be implemented and what resources will be required			
6. Demonstrates clearly that the benefits of the plan outweigh the possible objections to it			

Structure and Form			
7. Uses clear, precise words to express ideas			
8. Presents ideas in a logical sequence			

Grammar, Usage, and Mechanics			
9. Contains no more than two or three minor errors in spelling, capitalization, and punctuation			
10. Contains no more than two or three minor errors in grammar and usage			

Writing Progress to Date (Writing Portfolio)

The strongest aspect of this writing is _____

_____

The final version shows improvement over the rough draft in this way: _____

_____

A specific improvement over past assignments in your portfolio is_____

_____

A skill to work on in future assignments is_____

_____

Additional comments: _____

_____

CHAPTER 22

Dramatic Scene

Writing Workshop

Prewriting

More than other written forms of storytelling, a dramatic scene is about character. A good way to begin writing a dramatic scene is to imagine two interesting characters and then put them together.

Below, make a list of problems your two characters might be facing. Then figure out what each character most wants or needs. Finally, see if any of their desires come into conflict with each other. Conflicting desires offer natural material for a dramatic scene. (For example, an athlete's desire to be a star may conflict with a coach's desire for teamwork.)

Character 1	Character 2
Problems	**Problems**
1. _____ _____	1. _____ _____
2. _____ _____	2. _____ _____
3. _____ _____	3. _____ _____
Needs/Desires	**Needs/Desires**
1. _____ _____	1. _____ _____
2. _____ _____	2. _____ _____
3. _____ _____	3. _____ _____

CHAPTER 23

For use with Pupil's Edition pp. 438–445

Dramatic Scene

Writing Workshop

Drafting and Elaboration

In the opening of the scene below, the writer has provided only the barest introduction to the characters and setting. Use the Suggestions for Elaboration, the details in the Reader's Notebook, and ideas of your own to develop the opening.

Draft

Characters: Hank, *a student, age 16*

Ms. Delfo, *a phys. ed. teacher*

Setting: *A class of students in the gym. Ms. Delfo stands before them.*

Ms. Delfo. I need a volunteer to help me demonstrate the tango. (pause)

Henry, you will do just fine.

Hank. If you insist, Ms. Delfo.

Suggestions for Elaboration

• Describe Hank and Ms. Delfo in detail: dress, attitude, bearing.

• Use detailed description of setting to establish a mood.

• Use stage directions to indicate how dialogue is to be spoken.

• Use actions and dialogue to reveal character.

READER'S NOTEBOOK

■ Even in his gym outfit, Hank is obviously a punk: he has the haircut, the holes in his clothes, the sneer. ■ Ms. Delfo wears pink sweats and a tireless smile. ■ The gym is decorated for the coming prom, bunting swooping from the ceiling, a disco ball hanging over the floor. ■ Ms. Delfo's request evokes utter silence from the students. ■ Ms. Delfo always chirps girlishly; Hank usually mumbles and is sarcastic. ■ Ms. Delfo is light on her feet; Hank shuffles.

CHAPTER 23

Dramatic Scene

Peer Response Guide

There are so many elements involved in a dramatic scene—setting, character, dialogue, action, stage directions, plot, and more—that it can be difficult to know how successful you've been in juggling all the parts. To find out how your scene is working, ask a classmate to read it and answer the questions below.

1. What do you think of how the scene begins? How can this be improved?

Response:

Suggestions for Revision:

2. How would you describe the characters?

Response:

Suggestions for Revision:

3. Do the characters seem believable to you? Why or why not?

Response:

Suggestions for Revision:

For use with Pupil's Edition pp. 438–445

Dramatic Scene

Writing Workshop

Peer Response Guide *continued*

4. Are there any stage directions you think should be added or removed? If so, where?

Response:

Suggestions for Revision:

5. What parts of the scene, if any, are confusing to you?

Response:

Suggestions for Revision:

6. What do you think of the way the scene ends? Does it seem a fitting close, or did it leave you unsatisfied?

Response:

Suggestions for Revision:

CHAPTER 23

Dramatic Scene

Writing Workshop

Revising, Editing, and Proofreading

Revising

TARGET SKILL ➤ Considering Tone and Voice

When revising your dramatic scene, ask yourself the following questions:

- Have I used precise stage directions to keep the voice of each character consistent with her or his personality?

- Have I introduced the setting and characters in the opening stage directions?

- Have I used the setting and characters to create a convincing world?

- Have I developed a clear and interesting situation or conflict?

Editing and Proofreading

TARGET SKILL ➤ Formatting a Script

Use the bulleted list of suggestions below to edit and proofread the following passage from a draft of a dramatic scene between a student and a gym teacher. Correct errors in grammar, usage, mechanics, and spelling using proofreading marks. Pay particular attention to format.

- Set off names of speakers so that actors can find their parts readily.

- Remove quotation marks from dialogue; speaking directions should follow the name of the character.

- Place directions for actions where the action occurs.

- Use contractions to represent natural speech.

Draft

Ms. Delfo says, "What is wrong with your feet, Henry?"

Hank replies, "Nothing is wrong with my feet, Ms. Delfo."

Ms Delfo asks, "Then why are you not following my lead?" (*They have been attempting to dance to recorded tango music.*)

Hank answers, "It is a long and woeful story, Ms. Delfo. It begins with my dad, who used to take my ma dancing. When he decamped on my sixth birthday, my dear ma made me promis never to dance. (*He smurks, he is sarcastic.*)

Ms. Delfo responds, "I do not believe you."

Applying

Now edit and proofread your own dramatic scene. Refer to the bulleted list above.

For use with Pupil's Edition pp. 438–445

Dramatic Scene

Strong Student Model

Writing Workshop
These writing models are also
available in Assessment Masters.

A Lady's Day in Court

Characters

Tim, a 17-year-old basketball team hopeful
Steph, a 17–year-old cheerleader, valedictorian, all-around perfect student
Geek Chorus, three students who comment on the action. They want to be on the team but are not good players.

1. Introduces characters and setting in opening stage directions.

Scene

Tim *and the* Geek Chorus *are shooting baskets in preparation for tryouts. As the lights come up, they are taking shots, standing around in their sweat clothes, and passing basketballs. The basket is off-stage, out of sight. Tim throws the ball as the scene begins but winces and hides his face.*

Geek Chorus. That was a brick, man! Shoot like that, and the only position you'll get will be in the bricklayers' union. *(Their tone changes.)* But maybe it was the lady on the court distracting you, eh, Tim? *(They chortle.)*

2. Uses stage directions to indicate changes in dialogue focus.

Tim. *(seeing Steph and gulping)* Stephanie? What are you doing here?

Steph. *(above it all)* Oh, I'm just trying out for the team.

Geek Chorus. *(laugh loudly, shove each other, etc.)* Maybe she's come back for a little one-on-one with the guy whose heart she broke!

3. Dialogue of Geek Chorus reveals information about main characters.

Tim. *(sourly)* Cut it out, guys. Steph, it's a boys' team.

Steph. I'm a match for any boy. Or are you afraid of being shown up by a girl?

Tim. *(boastful)* Not much chance of that.

Steph. *(casual)* I don't know. The way I remember it, you seemed pretty defeated when I told you I wasn't going with you to the dance, even though *I* invited *you.* So defeated that you didn't hang around to hear why.

4. Her personality and their hidden conflict are revealed in her dialogue.

Tim. *(throwing basketball at her)* Why don't you start? One-on-one? To five?

Steph. *(smiling coldly)* You're on. *(She dribbles circles around Tim.)*

5. His personality and avoidance of hidden conflict are revealed in his actions and dialogue.

Geek Chorus. *(amazed)* She dribbles without looking! Sends the ball behind her back! Her technique is flawless! The Timster is in trouble!

CHAPTER 23

Dramatic Scene

Writing Workshop

Strong Student Model *continued*

Tim. *(huffing)* Letting me beat you in basketball won't square things between us, Steph—you know that, don't you?

Steph. *(laughing)* All *I* know is that I'm a point up. *(She spins and shoots.)*

Geek Chorus. *(in awe)* A turnaround jump shot! A swish through the net! Where'd she learn those moves?

Tim. *(taking the ball)* Beginner's luck. Doesn't mean you're anything special.

Steph. *(effortlessly steals ball)* No, it just means that you refuse to see the obvious. Exactly like before. *(She zooms toward the basket.)*

Geek Chorus. Oh, my gosh! Look at her go! It's hang time! It's a slam dunk! She's flying!

Tim. *(really angry now)* Oh, what didn't I see when you dumped me? That you were too good for me? *(He drives hard for the basket. He misses.)*

Steph. *(She gets the rebound, runs off, then hooks ball over her shoulder.)*

Geek Chorus. Call an ambulance! Tim is getting murdered out there!

Tim. *(looks near tears)* Three to zip. But not for long. (cautiously moves toward basket)

Steph. (blows bangs off forehead) Whatever. *(She casually reaches out, snags ball, and flips it into basket.)*

Tim. *(determined)* You're not going to do that again, you arrogant brat!

Steph. *(She steals the ball again and sinks it; the Geek Chorus moan and cover their faces.)* That's five. Game over.

Tim. *(falls to his knees, depressed)* Why are you doing this to me?

Steph. *(passionate for the first time)* Because you don't listen! I didn't go with you to the dance because I *can't* dance. I tried to tell you, but you—

Tim. *(hopeful)* You can't dance?

Steph. *(embarrassed)* I was ashamed.

Tim. *(smiling)* So it wasn't me?

Steph. *(exasperated)* No, you twit. Though if I'd known you can't play basketball, it might have been a different story. *(She reaches a hand down and helps him up.)* Ready to stop wasting time?

Tim. Yeah. Let's get out of here. *(He tosses ball to the Geek Chorus.)* Good luck, guys. *(Tim and Steph exit.)*

Geek Chorus. *(sadly)* Why do we always end up alone?

6. Dialogue of Geek Chorus reveals what is happening off-stage.

7. Shows how Tim's anger cripples his play in the game as it did his response to the conflict over the dance.

8. Reversal of audience expectations makes both characters more sympathetic.

9. Dialogue changes to reflect reversal in plot, revealing warmth between characters.

10. Uses actions and dialogue to end scene on a note of completion.

For use with Pupil's Edition pp. 438–445

CHAPTER 23

Dramatic Scene

Writing Workshop

Average Student Model

One-on-One

Characters

Tim, *a 17-year-old student*
Steph, *a 17-year-old student*
Rob, *a friend of* Tim's *who comments on the action*

Scene

As the lights come up, Tim *and* Rob *are shooting baskets in preparation for tryouts. The basket is off-stage, out of sight.* Tim *throws the ball as the scene begins.*

Rob. That was a lame shot, man—you completely missed! Maybe it was thoughts of Stephanie dumping you that threw off your aim. *(chortles)*

Tim. *(pretending to be carefree)* Stephanie? Who are you talking about?

Rob. That girl who broke your heart. That girl who wouldn't go with you to the dance. That girl who is right behind you. (Rob turns away.)

Tim. *(gulps)* Steph? What are you doing here?

Steph. *(above it all)* Oh, I'm just trying out for the team.

Rob. Maybe she's come back to finish the number she did on you, man!

Tim. *(sourly)* Shut it, Rob. Steph, it's a boys' team.

Steph. I'm a match for any boy. Or are you afraid of being shown up by a girl?

Tim. *(boastful)* That's never been a problem before.

Rob. *(laughing and snickering)* Except when she dumped you! When she—

Tim. I get the idea, Rob.

Steph. *(casual)* He's right. The way I remember it, you seemed pretty defeated when I told you I wasn't going with you to the dance.

Tim. I was upset. So what? *(tosses basketball to her)* One-on-one? To five?

Steph. *(smiling coldly)* You're on. (She dribbles circles around Tim.)

Rob. *(amazed)* Wow, can she move!

Tim. *(huffing)* I can beat you easy!

Steph. Whatever you say, Tim. *(laughing)* I'm a point up. *(She shoots.)*

1. Introduces characters and setting in opening stage directions but without much character background.

2. Uses dialogue to indicate entrance of character.

3. Uses stage directions to show how dialogue should be spoken.

4. Secondary character's dialogue fills in background about main characters.

5. Characters' actions and dialogue reveal personalities and conflict.

CHAPTER 23

Dramatic Scene

Writing Workshop

Average Student Model *continued*

Rob. *(in awe)* Nice jump shot!

Tim. *(taking the ball)* Beginner's luck.

Steph. *(steals ball)* Call it whatever you want. *(She zooms toward the basket.)*

Rob. Oh, my gosh! Look at her go! She's flying!

Tim. *(really angry now)* Are you so mean that you won't be satisfied with humiliating me? You have to demolish me on the basketball court, too? *(He drives hard for the basket. He misses.)*

Steph. *(She gets rebound, runs off, then hooks ball over her shoulder.)*

Rob. That would be a three-pointer! If this was a full-court game, I mean.

Tim. *(looks near tears)* Fine, three to zip. *(He cautiously moves toward basket.)* Are you trying to pay me back for something?

Steph. *(She casually reaches out, snags ball, and flips it into basket.)* No, I'm just trying to get your attention, Tim. You were so upset when I broke off our date that you never gave me a chance to explain why.

Tim. You're right, I didn't. I guess that was bad, but I was so angry and hurt that I didn't want to see you. *(He gets ball, looks determined.)* You're not going to steal the ball again—

Steph. *(She steals ball, sinks it; Rob covers his face.)* That's five. Game over.

Tim. *(cautiously)* Maybe I was judging you too harshly. Can you forgive me?

Steph. *(emotional for the first time)* You're forgiven, Tim! I didn't go with you to the dance because I can't dance. I tried to tell you, but you—

Tim. *(hopefully)* You can't dance?

Steph. *(embarrassed)* I was ashamed.

Tim. *(smiling)* So it wasn't me?

Steph. *(exasperated)* No, you twit. Though if I'd known you can't play basketball, it might have been a different story. *(She reaches out to him with both hands.)* Ready to stop wasting time?

Tim. Yeah. Let's get out of here. *(He and Steph exit.)*

6. Dialogue of secondary character reveals what is happening off-stage.

7. Her dialogue explains the conflict but is so direct that it is unrealistic.

8. His dialogue, too, is unrealistic; his anger is suddenly replaced by regret.

9. He apologizes even before she explains her problem, thus weakening the dramatic climax. Resolution of conflict is too abrupt.

10. Uses actions and dialogue to end scene.

CHAPTER 23

Dramatic Scene

Writing Workshop

Weak Student Model

A Basketball Game

Characters
Three seventeen-year-old students:
Tim, Steph, *and* **Rob**

Scene
School gym. Tim *and* Rob *are shooting baskets in preparation for tryouts. The basket is off-stage, out of sight.* Tim *throws the ball as the scene begins.*

   Rob. That was a lame shot. You shoot like a girl. If you keep playing like that, Coach Winters will never put you on the team.

   Tim. Man, I want to get on the team bad. Ever since Steph broke up with me, the thought of the basketball team is the only thing that has kept me from thinking I am a total loser.

   Rob. Are you still crying over that? Buck up, my friend; there are other fish in the sea. Don't let thoughts of her disrupt your game.

   Steph. He's right, Tim—you shouldn't let thoughts of me disrupt your game.

   Tim. Steph? What are you doing here?

   Steph. I'm trying out for the team.

   Rob. She's probably come to twist the knife, Tim.

   Tim. Steph, it's a boys' team.

   Steph. I'm a match for any boy.

   Tim. I bet you can't beat me.

   Steph. I will happily play you a game, Tim. But I do feel bad about this, since I have already broken your heart. It will be worse if I then win against you in basketball. I do not want to take away every last shred of your masculinity. I have already turned you down for the dance, and your reaction was very disheartening. I don't want to humiliate you here on the court.

   Tim. But Steph! I was crushed. I was in love with you, and then on the night of the dance when I showed up at your house, you reneged without explaining why. What could I do but be angry?

   Steph. You never permitted me to explain why I wasn't able to go to the dance. You just began shouting and wouldn't let me get a word in edgewise. Then you drove away in your car when I ran to the bathroom to cry. And you haven't answered my calls since then.

1. Title has little relation to scene; no game is ever played.

2. Cites character names and setting without explanation of who each character is.

3. Uses dialogue to fill in background but in an unrealistic manner.

4. Stage directions would be useful here to show Steph's entrance.

5. Secondary character's dialogue reveals tension between main characters.

6. Misses opportunity here to have actions show characters' moods.

7. The dialogue is unrealistic because it is so explicit and lengthy (few real people make such speeches unless they are at a lectern).

8. Having the characters allude to their conflict is a good idea, but the dialogue is unnaturally stiff.

Dramatic Scene

Weak Student Model *continued*

Tim. I was too upset.

Steph. I understand, Tim, but . . .

Tim. Is that why you're here today? To make me talk to you?

Steph. No, I'm just trying to get your attention, Tim. I hoped you would let me explain.

Tim. Maybe I was judging you too harshly. Can you forgive me?

Steph. You're forgiven, Tim! I didn't go with you to the dance because I can't dance. I tried to tell you, but you—

Tim. You can't dance?

Steph. No, and I was ashamed.

Tim. So it wasn't because of me?

Steph. Not at all. It was because I was having a panic attack before the dance and was just freaking out. If I had been more mature, I would have just come right out and told you what the problem was instead of hemming and hawing.

Tim. And if I had been more mature, I would have let you explain everything at your own pace instead of running away in a snit.

Steph. Oh, Tim, I'm so happy we're talking again. Are you ready to stop wasting time?

Rob. Go ahead, Tiger. I'll stay here and tell Coach you'll be back for tryouts on another day.

Tim. Okay. Come on, Steph—let's get out of here! (He and Steph exit.)

9. Resolution does not surprise or satisfy because no conflict was developed.

10. Ending seems incomplete and artificial.

11: Scene lacks real conflict; lacks stage directions; setting is never used; there is little action, only stilted dialogue.

For use with Pupil's Edition pp. 438–445

Dramatic Scene

Writing Workshop

Rubric for Evaluation

Ideas and Content	Weak	Average	Strong
1. Introduces the setting and characters in the opening stage directions			
2. Uses the setting and characters to create a convincing world			
3. Develops a clear and interesting situation or conflict			
4. Reveals the personalities of the characters through dialogue			

Structure and Form			
5. Uses actions as well as dialogue to advance the story			
6. Includes stage directions as necessary			

Grammar, Usage, and Mechanics			
7. Contains no more than two or three minor errors in spelling, capitalization, and punctuation			
8. Contains no more than two or three minor errors in grammar and usage			

Writing Progress to Date (Writing Portfolio)

The strongest aspect of this writing is _____

_____

The final version shows improvement over the rough draft in this way: _____

_____

A specific improvement over past assignments in your portfolio is_____

_____

A skill to work on in future assignments is_____

_____

Additional comments: _____

_____

CHAPTER 23

Research Report   *Writing Workshop*

Prewriting

To begin your research paper, follow the steps outlined below.

- **Choose a topic:** To help choose and narrow a topic for your research report, fill in and extend the cluster map shown below. Once you have narrowed your general topic, set your goal, identify your purpose, and write a statement of controlling purpose.

- **Set your goal:** (Check at least one.)
  - ❏ to learn more about your subject   ❏ to prove a point
  - ❏ to elicit a strong response from your audience

- **Identify your purpose:** (Check at least one.)
  - ❏ to inform   ❏ to compare and contrast
  - ❏ to examine cause and effect   ❏ to analyze

- **Write a statement of controlling purpose:** State the focus of your research report. _____

_____

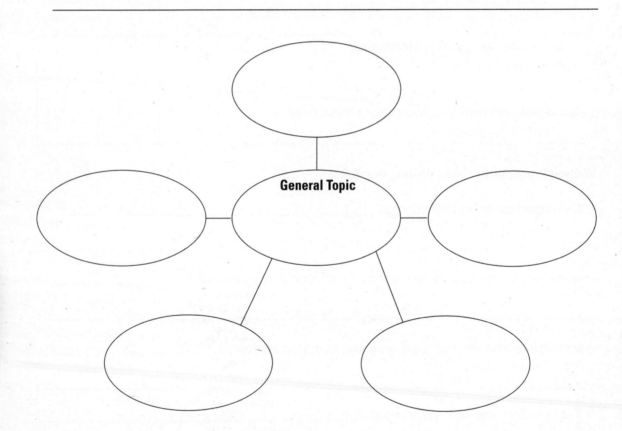

For use with Pupil's Edition pp. 448–461

CHAPTER 24

Research Report

Writing Workshop

Drafting and Elaboration

When you finish your research, you will have a clearer idea of what you want your research report to accomplish. Your report, like many other essays, will begin with a thesis statement that expresses your main idea. The largest part of your report, the body, should explain and support your topic.

The passage below is from the draft of a student's research report about the Globe Theatre. It does not include enough details and examples. To make the paragraph more vivid, follow the Suggestions for Elaboration listed below and use information from the Reader's Notebook. Write your revised paragraph on a separate sheet of paper.

Draft

If you wanted to see a play written by William Shakespeare 400 years ago, you had to go to a certain theater. Many plays were performed there. The theater was not square but almost round. The stage stuck out into the middle of the floor. The Elizabethan audience really liked the stage area because it was like heaven and hell.

Suggestions for Elaboration

- Name the theater where Shakespeare's plays were performed 400 years ago.
- Give an example of one of Shakespeare's plays.
- Give a more detailed description of the inside of the theater.
- Clarify why the stage seemed symbolic of heaven and hell.

READER'S NOTEBOOK

■ Shakespeare's plays were staged at the Globe Theatre. ■ *Henry IV* is one of Shakespeare's plays. ■ The theater had three separate entrances to the stage. ■ Trap doors allowed props and actors to rise from the floor. ■ An elevated area behind and above the stage was sometimes used as a balcony. ■ The loft represented heaven, and the trap door led to hell.

CHAPTER 24

Research Report

Peer Response Guide

Have you found an interesting topic, researched it thoroughly, and presented your information clearly? To find out if your research report achieves the goal you set, share your report with a classmate and ask the following questions.

1. What did you like best about my report?

Response:

Suggestions for Revision:

2. What two or three main things did you learn from my report?

Response:

Suggestions for Revision:

3. What things would you still like to learn from my report?

Response:

Suggestions for Revision:

For use with Pupil's Edition pp. 448–461

CHAPTER 24

Research Report

Writing Workshop

Peer Response Guide *continued*

4. What parts of the report did not flow smoothly or seemed confusing?

Response:

Suggestions for Revision:

5. What one thing would you suggest that might help me write a better report next time?

Response:

Suggestions for Revision:

6. What impression were you left with after you read my conclusion?

Response:

Suggestions for Revision:

Research Report

Revising, Editing, and Proofreading

Revising

TARGET SKILL ➤ Improving Thesis Statements

As you revise your research report, ask yourself the following questions:

• Does my thesis statement fit my paper properly?

• Have I followed a logical pattern of organization, with transitions between ideas?

• Did I present evidence from primary and secondary sources to develop and support ideas?

• Did I credit sources of information?

Editing and Proofreading

TARGET SKILL ➤ Punctuating Appositives

Refer to the bulleted list to help you edit the following paragraph from a student's research report on the Globe Theater. Use proofreading marks to correct errors in grammar, usage, mechanics, and spelling. Then copy your corrected draft onto a clean sheet of paper.

• Place a comma at the beginning of a nonessential appositive, and place a matching comma at the end unless the appositive ends a sentence.

• Eliminate any sentence that does not support the central idea.

• Clarify sentences by correcting verb tense errors.

• Correct any misplaced or dangling modifiers.

Draft

The first theater in england enjoyed by many enthusiastic playgoers was built in 1576. Before then, most plays are performed by travelling theater groups. I don't know what the plays were. Set up at one end of an inn yard, the plays were performed outside on a stage. The position of the stage allows the audience to surround the stage on three sides. There was no curtain which normally marks a boundary between the stage and the audience.

Applying

Now edit and proofread your own research report. Refer to the bulleted list above.

Research Report

Strong Student Model

Writing Workshop

*These writing models are also available in **Assessment Masters**.*

John Williams
Ms. Burns
English IV
19 May 2001

Williams 1

The Globe: A Theater for All People

Modern theatergoers who want to see a production of one of Shakespeare's plays have several options. They can go to a conventional theater with famous actors, attend a high school production, see an outdoor performance, or even rent a video and watch a movie version of the play in the comfort of their own home.

Have you ever wondered what it would have been like, 400 years ago, to experience one of Shakespeare's plays "hot off the press"?

Before 1576, when the first theater in England was built, most plays had been performed by traveling theater groups in inn yards. Galleries or balconies circled this courtyard from the second and third stories. The actors set up a platform stage at one end of the inn yard, which was surrounded by the audience on three sides. There was no curtain.

Public theaters built in London during Shakespeare's lifetime generally followed the same pattern. The Globe Theatre was built in 1599. The theater was shaped like a polygon, with thatched galleries. There was no roof (except over part of the stage and the balconies), and the floor was bare ground. Behind the stage were the dressing rooms, and above the stage was a canopy to keep off the sun and the rain. There were three separate entrances to the stage, which jutted out into the middle of the floor. Trapdoors allowed props and actors to rise from the floor. An elevated area behind and above the stage could be used as a balcony. There was no scenery to speak of, so audiences had to imagine the changes of scene.

For the Elizabethan audience, the stage was symbolic of the universe. The loft was called the "heavens"—from it gods might drop. Devils could spring through the trapdoor from the "hell" beneath the stage. Between heaven and hell was the stage, or solid earth, where most of the action of the drama took place. (Beckerman, 28)

1. The writer provides a title that focuses on the report's topic.

2. The writer begins with contemporary examples and then presents the thesis in the form of an intriguing question.

3. Uses transitional sentences between paragraphs to connect ideas.

4. Identifies source of information.

CHAPTER 24

Research Report

Writing Workshop

Strong Student Model *continued*

Williams 2

Actors were constantly rehearsing, as a company usually offered as many as 30 plays during the course of a year. There were no female actors in London. Instead, specially trained boys played the parts of women. They learned to walk and dress and speak as women, and they were thoroughly convincing.

On any given day when the flag flew above the Globe to announce a performance, several hundred people packed the theater, which was only about 60 feet wide by 60 feet long. The galleries were for aristocrats and merchants, those who could afford to pay threepence for the price of a seat. Most theatergoers, however, paid a penny for the privilege of standing on the floor. They were called "groundlings."

Going to the theater was a social event. People really enjoyed the eating and the socializing that took place. Some people, however, became rowdy. For example, if the audience members didn't like the play or an actor, they didn't hesitate to boo and hiss. As one historian has noted, "the theater was part and parcel of the active, feverish, and reckless social life of the time." (Cheney, 272)

Shakespeare and others wrote especially for the "groundlings," thus making the experience of theater rambunctious and lively. But as time went on, plays began to be performed in enclosed private theaters and for a higher price, which excluded the bulk of the Globe Theatre's audience. More and more, theatergoers were the wealthy, and plays were written to suit their tastes.

Works Cited

Beckerman, Bernard. "Shakespeare's Theatre." <u>William Shakespeare: The Complete Works</u>. Ed. Harbage, Alfred. Baltimore: Penguin Books, 1969.

Bentley, G.E. "William Shakespeare." <u>The World Book Encyclopedia</u>. 1997 ed.

Cheney, Sheldon. <u>The Theatre: Three Thousand Years of Drama, Acting, and Stagecraft</u>. New York, London, and Toronto: Longmans, Green and Co., 1952.

Hughes, Glenn. "Theater." <u>The World Book Encyclopedia</u>. 1997 ed.

Quennell, Peter. <u>Shakespeare: A Biography</u>. Cleveland and New York: The World Publishing Company, 1963.

---

5. The writer uses a direct quotation to support an idea. Other Options:
- Paraphrase the quotation.
- Summarize the information.

6. The conclusion restates the thesis.

7. Works Cited:
- Identifies sources of information used in researching a paper.
- Alphabetizes entries by author's last name.
- Lists complete publication information.
- Punctuates entries correctly.
- Follows a consistent style.

For use with Pupil's Edition pp. 448–461

CHAPTER 24

Research Report

Average Student Model

John Williams   Williams 1
Ms. Burns
English IV
19 May 2001

The Globe Theatre

Modern theatergoers who want to see a
Shakespeare play have several options. They can watch
actors in a regular theater. They can go to a high school
production, they can see a production in the park, or they
can even rent a video of a play. Some people have
Shakespeare readings in private homes. Each person
brings a copy of the play and reads a different part from
their own copy.

"The first theater in England was built in 1576."
Before that, most plays were being performed by
traveling theater groups in inn yards. There was no
curtain. Galleries or balconies ran around this courtyard at
the second and third stories. The actors set up a platform
stage at one end of the inn yard. The stage was
surrounded by the audience on three sides.

What was it like, 400 years ago, to see one of
Shakespeare's plays "hot off the press"?

Public theaters built in London during Shakespeare's
lifetime generally followed the same pattern. The Globe
Theatre, the "Wooden O," as it is referred to in the play
Henry IV, was built in 1599. The theater was shaped
almost like a circle, with thatched galleries. There was no
roof (except over part of the stage and the balconies),
and the floor was bare ground. Behind the stage were
the dressing rooms. There was a canopy over the stage.
The stage jutted out into the middle of the floor. There
were trapdoors in the floor for actors to use and to get
props to the stage. There were three separate entrances
onto the stage. There was also an elevated balcony-like
area.

"In the fullest sense, the stage itself was an emblem
of the universe. The loft above the stage, located under
the shadow or half-roof, was termed the "heavens." Out
of it gods might drop. The space beneath the stage was
the hell out of which devils might spring. . . . Between
heaven and hell rose the facade of earthly life." (28)

1. Since the
quotation is not
especially memorable
or lively, it would
have been better to
paraphrase it.

2. The thesis
statement is
misplaced. It should
be the first or
second paragraph
of the paper.

CHAPTER 24

Research Report

Average Student Model *continued*

Williams 2

The flag flew above the theater to announce a play. Then a lot of people packed into the theater, which was only about 60 feet wide by 60 feet long. The galleries were for the rich, who could afford to pay threepence for the price of a seat, while to stand cost a penny.

If the audience members didn't like the play or an actor, they would boo and hiss. Going to the theater was social. "The theater was part and parcel of the active, feverish, and reckless social life of the time." (272) Some people became rowdy.

There were an average of 200 performances a year (24) unless the plague was sweeping London, during Lent and the hot summer weeks, or during a period of censorship by the government. Actors were constantly rehearsing. There were no women actors. Instead, boys played the parts of women. They gave convincing performances. A company usually offered up to 30 plays a year.

After the Globe burned down in 1613, the new Globe was built in a suburb of London, in an area frequently flooded by the Thames River. Near the theater was the Bear Garden. The actors in the theater had to raise their voices over the barking of dogs and the cheers of the audience in the Bear Garden.

Eventually, theater became less of a popular entertainment, when more plays were performed in enclosed private theaters for a higher price. People who could pay only a penny couldn't go any more.

Although the circumstances were uncomfortable, audiences got to see splendid performances with beautiful costumes. There was no scenery to speak of. The audience had to imagine the changes of scene. "On several occasions one producer is known to have spent twice as much for the costume of one actor as he paid the dramatist for the play in which the costume was worn." It was as though a new play today were combined with a fashion parade.

3. The writer has not fully credited the sources.
Other Options:
- Paraphrase the quotation.
- Summarize the information.

4. Information is disorganized. Paragraphs lack unity.

5. Needs a strong conclusion.

Works Cited

Beckerman, Bernard. Shakespeare's Theatre. <u>William Shakespeare: The Complete Works</u>.
Bentley, G.E. <u>The World Book Encyclopedia</u>.
Cheney, Sheldon. New York, London, and Toronto: Longmans, Green and Co. <u>The Theatre: Three Thousand Years of Drama, Acting, and Stagecraft</u>.
Quennell, Peter. <u>Shakespeare: A Biography</u>. Cleveland and New York: The World Publishing Company.
"Theater." <u>The World Book Encyclopedia</u>.

6. Works Cited:
- Does not list complete publication information.
- Does not punctuate entries correctly.
- Does not cite encyclopedia sources correctly.

For use with Pupil's Edition pp. 448–461

Research Report

Writing Workshop

Weak Student Model

John Williams
Ms. Burns
English IV
19 May 2001

Williams 1

Going to a Shakespeare Play

If you wanted to see a play written by William Shakespeare 400 years ago, you can go to a regular theater. You can go to a high school to see a performance, or see one in the park. Or if you want to see the play at home you can even rent a video. If you want, you can read a play with other people, if you bring your own copy and then read a part from your copy. <u>It was really different when Shakespeare was writing plays</u>.

"The first theater in England was built in 1576." Before then, most plays were put on by traveling theater groups. They put on the plays in inn yards. People really liked visiting with the actors after a show. galleries or balconies run around this courtyard at the second and third stories. The actors set up a platform stage at one end, and there is no curtain. The audiense was on three sides.

Public theaters built in London when Shakespeare lived were like this too, generally. The Globe theatre was built in 1599. But this theater wasn't square, but almost round. There was no roof except over part of the stage and the balconies and the floor was just ground. Behind the stage were the dressing rooms, over it a canopy. The stage stuck out into the middle of the floor. For the actors to use and to get props onto the stage, there were trapdoors, three separate entrances to the stage. There was an area like a balcony.

"In the fullest sense, the stage itself was an emblem of the universe. The loft above the stage, located under the shadow or half-roof, was termed the "heavens." Out of it gods might drop. The space beneath the stage was the hell out of which devils might spring. Between heaven and hell rose the facade of earthly life."

When there was going to be a show, the flag was put up so that people could see it. A whole bunch of people came. Some of them stood on the floor. They paid a penny. The galleries were for the rich people. They could afford it.

1. This writer uses shifting verb tenses. Needs sentence variety.

2. Thesis statement is weak and poorly placed.

3. Includes spelling, capitalization, and punctuation errors.

4. Quoted material is not credited.

5. Information is incomplete and disorganized; there are several spelling and capitalization errors.

CHAPTER 24

Research Report

Weak Student Model *continued*

Williams 2

Some people became rowdy. If the audiense members didn't like the play or an actor, they complained by making a lot of noise. Going to the theater was a social thing.

There were no women actors. Boys played the parts of women, and they looked and acted just like women. There were an average of 200 performances a year. Actors were rehearsing all the time. They put on maybe thirty plays every year.

The new Globe was built in a suburb of London, in an area frequently flooded by the thames River. This was after the first Globe burned down. Near the theater was the Bear Garden. The actors in the theater had to shout sometimes because of the dogs attacking the bears and the audiense watching them that made so much noise.

After a while, more plays were performed in enclosed private theaters for a higher price. Poor people couldn't afford to go to the theater as much as before. Then they only had to pay a penny. Only the rich people could go now.

The audiense really like to see the beautiful costumes. Actors dressed up in wonderful costumes. There wasn't much scenery, and they had to imagine it. Sometimes actors paid more for costumes than for new plays from shakespeare and other writers. A play was sort of like a fashun show.

Going to see a Shakespeare play four hundred years ago was a lot different than it is now. It's hard even to imagine what it would be like.

6. This writer needs to restate thesis. Conclusion is weak. Another Option:
   - Summarize key points supporting thesis.

Works Cited

Bernard Beckerman Shakespeare's Theatre. <u>William Shakespeare: The Complete Works</u>.
G.E. Bentley <u>World Book</u>.
Peter Quennell <u>Shakespeare: A Biography</u>.
Sheldon Cheney. <u>The Theatre: Three Thousand Years of Drama, Acting, and Stagecraft</u>.
Theater. <u>The World Book Encyclopedia</u>.

7. Works Cited:
   - Does not alphabetize entries by author's last name.
   - Does not list complete publication information.
   - Does not punctuate entries correctly.

Research Report

Rubric for Evaluation

Ideas and Content	Weak	Average	Strong
1. Includes a strong introduction with a clear thesis statement			
2. Presents evidence from primary and secondary sources to develop and support ideas			
3. Credits sources of information			
4. Concludes with a satisfying summary of ideas			

Structure and Form			
5. Follows a logical pattern of organization			
6. Uses transitional words between ideas			
7. Includes a correctly formatted Works Cited list at the end			

Grammar, Usage, and Mechanics			
8. Contains no more than two or three minor errors in spelling, capitalization, and punctuation			
9. Contains no more than two or three minor errors in grammar and usage			

Writing Progress to Date (Writing Portfolio)

The strongest aspect of this writing is _____

_____

The final version shows improvement over the rough draft in this way: _____

_____

A specific improvement over past assignments in your portfolio is_____

_____

A skill to work on in future assignments is _____

_____

Additional comments: _____

_____

CHAPTER 24

Reference Works

Reference works are print materials that do not circulate from the library. Use reference works for authoritative information.

Encyclopedias can be **general** or **specialized.** General encyclopedias provide brief articles on general topics. Specialized encyclopedias contain in-depth articles on a specific topic.

Almanacs provide a source for current facts and statistics and may cover general topics or a particular subject.

Atlases are collections of bound maps, either for a specific region or for a particular kind of map, such as road maps.

Biographical dictionaries and **encyclopedias** contain articles about significant individuals.

The **vertical file** contains pamphlets, booklets, catalogs, and newspaper clippings filed by subject.

Identifying Sources

Which type(s) of source(s) would you consult to answer each of these questions?

1. Which writer won the Pulitzer Prize for fiction in 1983?

_____

2. What are the names of the bodies of water that border Denmark?

_____

3. What universities have agricultural departments?

_____

4. After whom was the cardigan sweater named?

_____

5. What Charles Dickens novel has a character named Pip?

_____

6. Who was George Washington Carver?

_____

7. How many undergraduates are enrolled at the local university?

_____

8. In what year did Ruholla Khomeini come to power in Iran?

_____

CHAPTER 25

For use with Pupil's Edition pp. 470–472

Evaluating Arguments

Good writers do more than collect facts—they try to derive meaning from those facts. When you evaluate information, the most important criterion for you to use is logic. Two methods writers can use to derive meaning are deductive and inductive reasoning. A **deductive** argument begins with a general statement of fact and draws specific conclusions from it. An **inductive** argument begins with specific facts or observations that lead to a general conclusion. This general conclusion often must be qualified, or limited in its scope.

A. Understanding Deduction

Study the following facts. Write the specific conclusion you can gather from each. If no conclusion is possible, write "none."

1. When a species' ability to survive is in question, that species is considered endangered. Endangered species quickly become extinct without protection. The ability of the California condor to survive is in question. _____

   _____

2. The Know-Nothing Party was formed to combat immigration in the 1840s. Many of the immigrants at that time were Roman Catholics. _____

   _____

3. Throughout history, the Quakers have been pacifists and abolitionists. The Grimké sisters, once Southern aristocrats, converted to the Quaker faith. _____

   _____

4. About 50 percent of marriages end in divorce. In 1940, 2 percent of marriages ended in divorce. In South Dakota, about 30 percent of marriages end in divorce. _____

   _____

B. Understanding Induction

Look for a relationship among the following sets of facts. Then write the conclusion that you reach.

1. Facts: Shakespeare wrote many tragic plays such as *Hamlet*.

   Shakespeare wrote many comic plays such as *As You Like It*.

   Shakespeare also composed many sonnets.

   Conclusion: _____

2. Facts: Dartmouth College is in Hanover, New Hampshire.

   Harvard University is in Cambridge, Massachusetts.

   Yale University is in New Haven, Connecticut.

   Dartmouth, Harvard, and Yale are Ivy League colleges.

   Conclusion: _____

Lesson 4

Detecting Logical Fallacies

An argument many seem to follow an inductive or deductive pattern and still not be valid—if it contains **logical fallacies,** or errors in the reasoning of your arguments. Learn to recognize such errors and to avoid them in your own speech and writing.

Ad hominem attacking the person, not the argument

Circular reasoning supporting a statement by repeating it in different terms

Evading the issue supporting an opinion without addressing the central point

Oversimplification omitting relevant information

Overgeneralization statement too broad to be true, often signaled by *always, completely,* or *never*

Either/or fallacy posing only two options and leaving no room for alternatives

False analogy comparing two things that are basically unlike

False cause attributing a result to a wrong cause

Identifying Logical Fallacies

Identify the logical fallacies in each of the following sentences.

1. Georgia O'Keeffe was a great painter because she was a gifted artist._____

_____

2. The boys' basketball team gets first choice of gym time because they're better than the

girls' team. _____

3. The Democrats won because they were well organized. _____

4. Fifty percent of the people in our town watched the governor's address on television; this

shows that half the townspeople are interested in politics._____

5. The tennis player performed incredibly—she was wearing HiEnergy tennis shoes._____

_____

6. Scott is a talented athlete. He'd be a natural team captain. _____

7. Since identical twins share the same genetic material, they are always talented in the same

ways. _____

8. Doberman pinschers are vicious dogs. _____

9. I can apply for the scholarship, or I can forget about going to art school altogether. _____

_____

For use with Pupil's Edition pp. 490–491

CHAPTER 26

Preparing for Debate

When debating a **proposition,** or topic, debaters must prepare a **brief** that accounts for the evidence and arguments of both sides of the proposition. Debaters must also prepare a **rebuttal,** or a follow-up speech to support the arguments and counter the opposition arguments.

Analyze the proposition, making sure it is clear and watching for words or phrases that your opponent might interpret differently.

Determine the issues, listing the reasons you have for supporting your side of the proposition and what you feel your opponents' contrasting reasons might be.

Choose your contentions, or main points, selecting those points that make the strongest case for your position.

Find and **choose** your evidence, selecting items that support each of your points.

Prepare an outline, using your main points as the main topics and your pieces of evidence as your subtopics.

A. Determining the Issues

Consider the proposition: *Resolved, that prisoners in penitentiaries should be allowed furloughs, or short periods of absences, for good behavior.* Decide which of the following arguments might be used by the opposing sides in a debate. Write either *affirmative* or *negative* in the blank.

1. Prisoners have been sent to penitentiaries for serious offenses, and their sentences should not be diminished by giving them leaves of absence._____

2. Prisoners' behavior will improve if they have the possibility of periodic furloughs during their incarceration._____

3. Prisoners occasionally need to have contact with the outside world to help them adjust to their eventual release._____

4. Good behavior in prison does not ensure good behavior in society._____

5. Fewer prison guards would be injured or killed if prisoners had the potential for furloughs based on good behavior._____

B. Finding and Choosing Your Evidence

On the lines below, list specific types of evidence that could be used to support the affirmative and negative sides of the proposition in Exercise A. Various types of evidence include statistics, examples, quotations from recognized authorities, and analogies to similar situations.

1. affirmative _____

_____

2. negative _____

_____

Lesson 6

Planning the Rebuttal Speech

A **rebuttal speech** is your opportunity to rebuild your case. Use these techniques when offering a rebuttal.

Listen to your opponent and note the points you wish to overturn.

Defend what the opposition has challenged.

Cite weaknesses or overlooked points in their arguments.

Present counterarguments and use more supporting evidence.

Offer summary arguments that restate and solidify your stance.

Preparing a Rebuttal Speech

You are on the negative team in a debate. Read the following constructive speech from the affirmative team. Then answer the questions, identifying each main argument and choosing the appropriate basis for your rebuttal.

(1) Suppose that a student walks into the principal's office and says, "I've heard that John Smith is dealing drugs." (2) Should the principal be allowed to search Smith—simply on the basis of this rumor? (3) We, the affirmative, believe that the administration should prohibit personal searches of students without probable cause.

(4) If someone accuses another person of an illegal act, the police cannot conduct a search unless the informant has some basis for his or her suspicions—such as actually seeing criminal activity. (5) This is the probable cause standard. (6) We believe subjecting students to a lesser standard relegates us to a position as second-class citizens. (7) When a student is searched, anything is fair game. (8) In one instance here, the principal even seized and read a student's personal journal while looking for evidence of drug dealing. (9) We believe that this is a clear invasion of privacy. (10) We also feel that the lack of protection against personal searches lays the groundwork for legal discrimination. (11) Suppose that a teacher has a grudge against a particular student or a student simply has a bad reputation.

(12) Therefore, we ask the administration to prohibit personal searches of students without probable cause.

1. Which sentence contains your opponents' first main argument? _____

   What basis for rebuttal could you use? _____

2. Which sentence contains your opponents' second main argument? _____

   What basis for rebuttal could you use? _____

3. Which sentence contains your opponents' third main argument? _____

   What basis for rebuttal could you use? _____

4. What alternative could you offer to your opponents' proposition? _____

   _____

For use with Pupil's Edition pp. 514–515

Context Clues

Lesson 1

CHAPTER 30

You can often get a clue to the meaning of an unfamiliar word from its **context,** the sentence or group of sentences in which the word appears. Different types of context clues are given below.

Definition or restatement meaning of the word is defined immediately after it. Signaled by dashes, commas, or words such as *or, that is, in other words.*

Example an example of a word follows the word. Signaled by *including, such as, for example.*

Contrast meaning of an unfamiliar word is suggested by what the word is not. Signaled by *however, but, although, by contrast, unlike.*

Cause and Effect either the cause or the effect are stated in familiar terms. Signaled by *as a result, because, since, when, therefore, consequently.*

Synonym unfamiliar word is followed by a familiar word with a similar meaning.

Structure repeated sentence pattern suggests associations between familiar and unfamiliar words.

Using Context Clues

Based on the context clues in the following sentences, define the boldfaced words.

1. **Mundane** subjects, ones that are common or ordinary, can become exciting when presented by a talented lecturer.

   _____

2. The **persimmon,** which is similar to a plum, is extremely sour unless it is fully ripe.

   _____

3. Because the toddler had walked at an early age, his parents concluded that he had an **aptitude** for athletics.

   _____

4. Good friends are usually **congenial;** for example, they enjoy the same activities and are interested in the same kinds of books.

   _____

5. King Louis XVI lived in **opulence,** unlike most of his subjects, who lived in poverty.

   _____

Lesson 2

Greek and Latin Roots

The specific meaning of a word root can help you determine the meaning of an unfamiliar word. For example, knowing that *therme* means "heat" helps you determine that *thermal* underwear can keep you warm. Many English words are derived from Greek and Latin roots.

Greek Roots	Meaning	Latin Roots	Meaning
anthrop	human	ali	other
bibl	book	anim	mind, life
bi, bio	life	corp	body
ge, geo	earth	dic, dict	say, tell
log	word, thought	grati	favor
micro	small	jus, jur	law, right
neo	new	lumin	light
phil	love	man	hand
phob	fear	sol	alone
phon	sound	temp	time
scope	seeing, looking at	termin	end, boundary
tele	far	un	one
therme	heat	vid, vis	see

Using Roots to Determine Meaning

Underline the root or roots in each of the following words and define each word. Then write one word that is based on the same root—in other words, that is in the same word family. Consult a dictionary as necessary.

1. gratifying _____

2. geostrophic _____

3. incorporate _____

4. microbiology _____

5. luminous _____

6. misanthrope _____

7. solitude _____

8. bibliophile _____

9. envision _____

10. phobia _____

For use with Pupil's Edition pp. 556–558

CHAPTER 30

Prefixes and Suffixes

You can determine the meanings of unfamiliar words by analyzing their prefixes, suffixes, base words, and roots. A **prefix** is a word part that is added to the beginning of a word or another word part. A **suffix** is a word part that is added to the end of a word or another word part. A **base word** is a complete word to which a prefix and/or suffix can be added. A **root** is a word part that cannot stand alone but to which a prefix and/or a suffix must be added. When word parts are combined, they form a new word with its own meaning.

Common Prefixes and Their Meanings

circum-	around	mal-	bad
com-, con-	with	mis-	wrong
equi-	equal	pre-	before
hypo-	under	re-	again
intra-	within	super-	above, beyond, more than
intro-	into	trans-	across

A **noun suffix** is added to a word or word part to create a noun.

Common Noun Suffixes and Their Meanings

-an	belong to, born in	-ment	result, state, condition
-ee	pertaining to	-ness	quality
-ics	science skill	-ist	doer, maker

An adjective suffix is added to a word or word part to create an adjective.

Common Adjective Suffixes and Their Meanings

-able	able, capable of being	-less	without
-ic	pertaining to	-ous	full of, having
-ish	like, similar	-ward	in the direction of

Using Prefixes and Suffixes with Base Words

In each word, underline the prefix or suffix once and underline the base word twice. Then, using the meanings of the word parts, write the meaning of the complete word on the line. Consult a dictionary if necessary.

1. inductee _____

2. circumnavigate _____

3. presuppose _____

4. equidistant _____

5. hypothesis _____

6. readable _____

7. malcontent _____

8. superimpose _____

9. intrastate_____

10. meteoric _____

Lesson 1

Preparing for College or Work

When you graduate, you will have to decide if you want to remain a student and attend college or begin working. Taking stock of your interests and options can help you make that decision.

A. Evaluating Options

Read the following description of a student. Then determine and list his career, school, and financial options.

An excellent all-around student, Juan writes articles for the school paper, participates in the debate club, and plays varsity basketball. He likes history and government best. Juan's parents can pay for in-state tuition only.

1. Possible careers/fields:_____

_____

2. Type of school: _____

_____

3. Financial plan:_____

_____

B. Identifying Your Interests and Needs

Answer the following questions to analyze which college and career options might be worth your investigation.

1. Do you like clearly defined tasks, or do you prefer more unstructured work?_____

_____

2. Do you prefer working with ideas, people, or tools? _____

3. Do you want to stay close to home after graduation, or would you like an opportunity to

travel to another city, state, or country?_____

4. What is your favorite school subject? What is it about the subject that you find

interesting?_____

5. What extracurricular activity gives you the most satisfaction? What are the qualities that

make it satisfying? _____

For use with Pupil's Edition pp. 570–571

CHAPTER 31

Applying to College

Your college application is your formal representative before the admissions committee, so make sure it represents you well. Read each application to ensure that you submit all the required items. As you fill out your application, check for accuracy, neatness, and conciseness. Also, be sure to mail it before the deadline date.

Planning an Application Essay

A college application may ask you to write an essay describing a personal achievement. Think about how you wish to present yourself. Then answer the questions below.

1. What personal qualities and characteristics make you proud of yourself? _____

_____

_____

_____

_____

2. What personal skills and abilities do you want the college to know you possess? _____

_____

_____

_____

3. Review your answers to questions 1 and 2. What personal achievement reflects those

answers? _____

_____

_____

_____

_____

_____

_____

4. On a separate sheet of paper, write an essay describing this achievement.

CHAPTER 31

Lesson 4

The Résumé

Most employers ask job candidates to send or bring a résumé. A **résumé** is a summary of your skills, experience, education, and other relevant information that is presented in an easy-to-read format. Always accompany your résumé with a cover letter.

Writing a Résumé

Decide what type of job you would like to seek; then use the following worksheet to gather information for your résumé. Write the résumé on a separate piece of paper.

1. **Name** _____ **Telephone** _____

2. **Address** _____

3. **Job Objective** _____

4. **Skills** _____

_____

_____

5. **Experience** (List each job, starting with most recent, and give the name and address of the company, dates employed, job title, and duties. Include volunteer work.)

_____

_____

_____

_____

_____

6. **Education** (Include all high schools attended, starting with the most recent; give school names, enrollment dates, selected courses of study, specialized training, and description of any awards received.)

_____

_____

7. **Personal Qualifications** (Include special talents, community activities, and other information about yourself.)

_____

_____

CHAPTER 31

For use with Pupil's Edition pp. 580–583

Applying for a Job

When you apply for a job, the first thing you usually do is send a résumé and cover letter to the company. A **cover letter** is written in business letter format and is addressed to a specific person, often the personnel director. Your cover letter is the first impression a prospective employer will have of you. It should state your purpose and list your qualifications for the position.

Writing a Cover Letter

You have decided to send your résumé in response to the following advertisement. Write a cover letter to accompany your résumé.

> **General Clerk**
> Major insurance company has opening for general clerk. Candidate must possess good communication and light typing skills. Duties include filing and handling telephone calls. Competitive starting salary and comprehensive benefit plan. Send résumé to Personnel Director, Acme Insurance Company, P.O. Box 460, Rockville, MD 20856.

1. Your Address and Date _____

_____

_____

2. Potential Employer's Name and/or Title and Address_____

_____

_____

_____

3. Salutation _____

4. Body _____

_____

_____

_____

_____

_____

_____

5. Closing _____

6. Signature _____

Answer Key

Grade 12, Chapter 11

Lesson 1, page 1

Answers will vary. Students should demonstrate an understanding of the techniques for focusing a topic. Ask the students which method they preferred and why.

Lesson 3, page 2

Possible answers:

1. talent show; chance to perform in front of an audience
2. local newspaper; attempt to make an impact on decision-makers and inform users of the library
3. Web site on oil; reach others with same interests
4. open-mic night; chance to practice live
5. local newspaper; notify friends and neighbors
6. Web site or zine; self-publish to share personal interests
7. online school newspaper or email; quickest way to send information to a large audience
8. school newspaper or yearbook; inform interested students
9. local or national writing contest; compete with other writers
10. online newspaper or bulletin board; persuade peers and reach a large audience

Grade 12, Chapter 12

Lesson 2, page 3

Possible answers:

1. The rain pounded hard on the roof, drowning out my radio. Through the droplets running in streams down the windowsill, I could see the tiny ash tree we planted last spring doubled over as if in pain. I wondered if it would make through the night. Even the great old oak creaked and groaned as it strained against the powerful gusts.
2. Each day, five percent of students will cut at least one class, if not the whole day. Students will try anything from writing phony hall passes to having friends call in and pretend to be a parent to miss class. If we are going to improve test scores and college acceptance rates, we need to get our students to stay in class.
3. Is it any wonder that Americans are following aerobic fitness regimens in record numbers? Aerobic exercise is one of the fastest and most effective ways to stay in shape and improve cardiovascular health.

Lesson 2, page 4

Answers will vary. Students should demonstrate an understanding of conclusions. Each conclusion should use a different method and should be interesting and coherent.

Lesson 3, page 5

Possible answers:

1. Spatial order, near to far: C, A, D, B, E
2. Order of importance, least to most significant: D, C, A, B or D, A, C, B

Lesson 4, page 6

A.

1. horse, it, animal, it
2. "war" appears six times

B.

Possible answer:

Almost everyone is familiar with the body of literature known as the Arthurian legends. Yet these legends are not the original tales first told in the Middle Ages. The tales have been influenced by many writers and have changed so much that few people now know what is fact and what is fiction. Even the legends themselves are contradictory.

The first area of disagreement focuses on who Arthur was. Legends say that he was born illegitimately of Uther Pendragon, a Welsh noble, and Igrayne, the wife of the duke of Gorlois. The magician Merlin supposedly took the infant to live with a lord named Ector but did not reveal the boy's royal heritage. Thirteen years later, after Uther died, Arthur performed the deed that was to designate him the new king. He pulled the sword Excalibur out of a stone.

According to early historical sources, however, Arthur was probably nothing more than a great leader of a Celtic tribe. The earliest reference to Arthur can be found in the anonymous poem *Gododdin* from the seventh century A.D. The Welsh historian Nennius told some of the first Arthurian tales in his *History of the Britons* and in the appendix to it, titled *Mirabilia*, or "Marvels."

Grade 12, Chapter 13

Lesson 1, page 7

Answers will vary. Students should demonstrate an understanding of elaboration techniques and use at least one in each paragraph. The paragraphs should be coherent and interesting. Encourage the students to be as creative as possible in their descriptions.

Lesson 3, page 8

Answers will vary. Students should demonstrate an understanding of how to use a quotation to enhance the meaning of an idea. Each paragraph should be coherent and interesting.

Chapter 14
Lesson 1, page 9
A. *Answers will vary. Possible answers:*
1. Zoos have evolved from gloomy collections for caged wild animals to important centers for wildlife education.
2. Television plays an important social role in society.

B. *Answers will vary. Possible answer:*
Handwriting is an important communication skill that will not be replaced by modern technology and should be learned at an early age.

Lesson 2, page 10
1. The many sides of the character of Falstaff
2. Falstaff's weight and age; his feelings of betrayal
3. No; the details should be in the same order as they are listed in the second sentence.
4. The audience should know what the Gadshill robbery incident was. They need more details about the fight from which Falstaff runs. They need to know who Hotspur was.

Lesson 4, page 11
Answers will vary. Possible answers:
1. Expecting to continue his mortal life, an Egyptian pharaoh was entombed with earthly belongings.
2. Radio City Music Hall, which seats 6,200 people, is the world's biggest movie theater, and the Rockettes perform there.
3. Because she wanted to become an engineer, Wendy applied to the engineering program at Cornell University, where she was accepted.
4. Acoma, New Mexico, was settled in 1075 and is the oldest continually inhabited U.S. town.
5. Edgar Allan Poe attended West Point, but he was dismissed for misbehavior.

Lesson 5, page 12
1. The chairperson of the board will be the keynote speaker at the luncheon.
2. The dried-up lake offered no relief from the stifling air.
3. The mail carrier delivered a new script to the actor's dressing room.
4. She silently crept though the dark hallway.

Lesson 6, page 13

Reggie looked quickly over his shoulder as he descended the stairs to the subway station. Behind him the street was dark and empty. ahead of him the platform was also empty, A testament to the late hour. Reggie suspected that the next train would be the last one of the night. He peered down the tracks and willed it to come. he didn't like riding the subway. he especially didn't like riding it alone late at night. Five minutes later there was a low rumble and a rush of air, and finally the train emerged out of the tunnel. Reggie sat on the long bench in the first car, and stared at the ads above the windows. The he noticed the other passenger. A heavyset young man in jeans and a T-shirt. The man wore a two-day stubble, sunglasses, and a smirk. He looked at Reggie from the far end of the car. Reggie looked away. At the first stop Reggie could see other people on the platform, but no one entered his car. At the second stop another young man in jeans and a T-shirt got on. He looked around. "Mike," he said to the other passenger. "Hey," said Mike, "How're you doin'?" The newcomer slouched into the seat next to Mike. The two looked at Reggie and then at each other. Reggie knew they were planning some thing.

Grade 12, Chapter 15
Lesson 1, page 14
A.
1. Formal English
2. Informal English

B.
Students should demonstrate an understanding of informal and formal English. If the students decide to rewrite the first example in informal English, be sure all grammar rules are applied. Students should use all the information given.

Lesson 2, page 15
Students should demonstrate an understanding of imagery and should show, not tell, what happened. Students should address at least two of the senses.

Lesson 2, page 16

A.
1. personification
2. hyperbole
3. simile
4. understatement
5. simile
6. hyperbole

B. *Possible answers:*
1. The coal miner's face was as dirty as a one-year-old's face after eating chocolate birthday cake.
2. The rats danced after the Piper, bobbing their heads to the music as he lead them out of town.
3. The field of sunflowers was so blinding I had to close my eyes and feel for my sunglasses in my backpack.
4. The waterfall of lava poured out of the fissure.

Lesson 3, page 17

Possible answers:
1. ironic: "in a bad way," "decadent," inevitably," "collapse"
2. breezy: "rushed away," "deeply, deeply excited," "wild with joy," "skip so high, run ... so fast," "do such daring things"
3. romantic: "breathlessness of attention," "bright and radiant," "of happiness, of hope, of brightness, warmth, and celebration"
4. ironic, humorous: "very highest birth," "their own free choice," "remained ... for years," "many years ago now"

Lesson 4, page 18
1. second person
2. first person
3. third person
4. first person

Lesson 5, page 19
Students should demonstrate an understanding of voice through their use of word choice, sentence length, and imagery.

Grade 12, Chapter 16

Lesson 2, page 20
1. air
2. Sentence 3
3. repetition
4. Sentence 2
5. parallelism
6. monster; strength and cunning

Lesson 3, page 21
Possible answers:
1. Daily, about ten million people worldwide celebrate their birthdays.
2. During the 1930s, one-third of all U.S. citizens lived on farms.

3. After we found the first few fossils, the dig became exciting.
4. To attract insects, the Venus flytrap emits a sweet smell.
5. For many years, scientists have studied the language of whales.
6. Until the law changed in the 1940s, children legally had to salute the flag.
7. Before they were made of pumpkins, jack-o'-lanterns were made of turnips.
8. Laughing and splashing, we ran across the puddles of water.

Lesson 4, page 22
Possible answers:
1. Not stopping for 64 hours, Norman Albert set a record for treading water.
2. Working day and night, the crew finished the renovations in a week.
3. The ospreys spend the summer in Scotland and migrate to Africa in winter.
4. Inside the deep, dark cave, she lit a match.
5. Vincent van Gogh completed more than 800 oil paintings but sold only one in his lifetime.
6. The referee missed the foul because he was looking the other way.
7. The Masai are herdsmen whose cattle are their most prized possessions.
8. Elliot, a talented painist, won the music competition.

Lesson 6, page 23

A.
1. onomatopoeia
2. alliteration
3. assonance
4. consonance

B. Students should demonstrate an understanding of sound devices. Encourage students to be creative.

Grade 12, Chapter 17

Application Essay
Drafting and Elaboration
Possible Response:

Between my freshman and sophomore years, my parents separated and divorced. It was a pretty depressing time for me, but it was a little easier for my sister because she kept so busy. Being more of a "social animal," she spent most of her time at cheerleading practice, in swim meets, or just hanging out with friends. Since she is two years older than me, I thought I had better listen when she said, "Mark, get a *life.* There's nothing you can do to change things, and you'll be a lot happier if you get out more." I soon learned that my sister was right; the only way to stop feeling sad and lonely was to start involving myself more in life.

Grade 12, Chapter 17

Application Essay
Revising, Editing, and Proofreading

Possible Response:

Everyone in my school, ~~including the weirdest~~
~~kids,~~ *is* ~~are~~ in some kind of clique. There are ~~the~~
punks and preps, jocks and drama types, ~~are~~
~~another kind, we have~~ motorheads and hippies,
~~and~~ skaters ~~are around, too. I could list groups~~
~~all day long.~~ For a long time, I thought no one
could have crossed over from one group to
another unless the *cliques* ~~clicks~~ were closely related.
~~For example, jocks might also be preps in some~~
~~special cases. But, basically,~~ jocks are jocks, *and*
~~∅~~eeks, *would always be* ~~have always been~~ geeks.

Grade 12, Chapter 18

Personality Profile
Drafting and Elaboration

Possible Response:

While still in his crib, Tiger watched his father,
who was an excellent golfer, hit golf balls into a
net. Even before he was out of his high chair,
Tiger began imitating his father's golf swing.
Tiger's talent quickly became so evident that,
when he was two, he appeared as a guest on
The Mike Douglas Show, putting with the host.
The budding athlete soon started breaking
records: at only three years old, Tiger shot 48
for nine holes, and at eight, he was winning
amateur golf championships. Then, during the
year when he turned 21, Tiger Woods became
the youngest Masters champion in history.

Grade 12, Chapter 18

Personality Profile
Revising, Editing, and Proofreading

Possible Response:

Tiger grew up hearing stories of Tiger Phong.
Phong was his father's best friend *with whom* ~~who~~ he had
fought ~~with~~ during the vietnam war. *but it* After they
~~ended,~~ *the two friends lost contact.* ~~his father lost contact with his friend.~~ *Tiger's* ~~His~~
father thought he could get in touch with his
friend to tell him about the birth of Tiger Woods.
Unfortunately, however, ~~But no,~~ His father's friend ~~dies~~ *had died* just eight
months after Tiger ~~is~~ *was* born.

Grade 12, Chapter 19

Critical Review of Literature
Drafting and Elaboration

Possible Response:

Gabriel looks at his wife, Gretta, as she sleeps,
and he notices that she is aging. This
observation makes Gabriel ponder the fact that
everyone will die; life is a long process that will
inevitably end in death. He contemplates
Michael Furey, a man who died long ago
because of his love for Gretta, Mary Jane's
pupils, and old Aunt Julia, who is near the end of
her life. Gabriel thinks that "one by one they
were all becoming shades," and his reverie
expands into a kind of vision. He imagines the
snow falling all over Ireland, falling upon the
cemeteries, falling "upon all the living and the
dead." The snow will continue to fall, shrouding
everything without regard for life or death, just
as people will continue to pass in and out of life.

Grade 12, Chapter 19

Critical Review of Literature
Revising, Editing, and Proofreading

Possible Response:

Gabriel looked at his wife while she was
sleeping and noticed that *she had* ~~his wife have~~ aged.
He thought about Michael Furey, once the
sweetheart of his wife, *Furey was* ~~∅~~long dead. One wet
and stormy night, the sickly young man had
come ~~came~~ to her garden, losing his life as a result.
Gabriel also thought about those others who had
died or were soon to die, ~~he thought~~ especially
~~about~~ his aunt Julia. Then his imagination
created a larger vision. He had a vision of all the
living and the dead, with the snow falling on *them* ~~it~~.

Grade 12, Chapter 20

Subject Analysis
Drafting and Elaboration

Possible Response:

Many drivers let their minds wander; they could
be thinking of anything from a problem at work
or an algebra exam at school to Friday's party or
Saturday's game. Not only do thoughts stray, but
people also try to do two things at once. You see
drivers applying mascara, combing their hair,
conducting an unseen orchestra, turning around
to talk to someone in the back seat, chatting on
the phone, or even shaving. As a result of these
distractions, people risk making mistakes that

can have disastrous consequences; they might fail to slow down at a dangerous curve or intersection. The result could be a traffic ticket or a dented fender, or it could be a major accident—bumps and bruises or a tragic fatality.

Grade 12, Chapter 20

Subject Analysis
Revising, Editing, and Proofreading
Possible Response:

Drivers often think their car parts are in fine condition so they neglect maintenance. Don't trust to luck. Have the engine, brakes, lights, and tires check by a mechanic. Keep each window clean so they give you the best possible visibility. Play your radio softly or it should be turned off if it becomes a distraction. Then pay attention to traffic and pedestrians when driving. You never knows whose life you might save.

Grade 12, Chapter 21

Business Writing
Drafting and Elaboration
Possible Response:

Kathleen Reslet
3406 Green Street
Ellingsworth, IL 60606
(773) 555-4567

Job Objective
Full-time employment as a radio deejay

Experience
- Deejay for WEHS, Elston High School's radio station
- Intern at WJAZ, Ellingsworth's local radio station
- Lead singer for Low Notes, a jazz and blues band that performs at coffee houses on weekends

Education and Honors
- Elston High School, Class of 2000
- Ellingsworth Community College, Radio/Communication Class, Spring, 2000

Activities and Interests
- Audio/Visual Club, president
- Drama Club, member and actor
- Deejay at friends' parties

Grade 12, Chapter 21

Business Writing
Revising, Editing, and Proofreading
Possible Response:

Job Objective
Full-time employment as a radio deejay
Radio station worker, full-time

Education and Honors
- Graduated and got a diploma from Elston high school, class of in the year 2000
- Ellingsworth Community College, Radio/Comunication class, in 2000

Activities and Interests
- Audio/Visual Club, president
- Drama Club, Member
- Deejay, at friends' parties and other places school dances

Grade 12, Chapter 22

Proposal
Drafting and Elaboration
Possible Response:

Many students want to work on their writing skills. According to a study by the National Center for Education Statistics, about 33 percent of eleventh graders keep a diary or journal outside of class, and 18 percent of them write stories or poems in their spare time. These statistics show an increase in percentages since 1984. Not only do students have a desire to write, but there is also evidence that certain practices can improve their writing skills. The National Assessment of Educational Progress shows that twelfth graders who make lists or outlines and complete more than one draft tend to write more proficiently than students who do not. It is not surprising that these methods are beneficial; outlining can be very helpful for organizing and condensing ideas, and revising is essential for catching mistakes and refining thoughts.

Grade 12, Chapter 22

Proposal
Revising, Editing, and Proofreading

Possible Response:

Organizing a writers program that allows each student to come into contact with ~~the~~ *visiting* writers ~~at who would be happy to visit~~ taft High School ~~during the time the program is being held~~ is a very good idea. ~~Such a cool thing~~ *A program like this would be extremely beneficial* for the students. ~~We could do~~ the program *would be held* throughout the whole school. The writers would stop by several diffrent English classes and do their writing workshops, *which would be* followed by a short question and answer period. Students could ask ~~them their~~ questions, and ~~they could answer them~~ *the visiting writers could give answers from their own experience*

Grade 12, Chapter 23

Dramatic Scene
Drafting and Elaboration

Possible Response:

Characters

Hank, *a student, age 16. Even in his gym clothes, Hank is obviously a punk: he has the haircut, the holes in his clothes, the sneer.*

Ms Delfo, *a gym teacher. She wears pink sweats and a tireless smile.*

Setting

Ms. Delfo stands before a class of students in the gym, which is decorated for the coming prom: bunting swoops from the ceiling and a disco ball hangs over the floor.

Ms. Delfo. *(Chirping girlishly)* I need a volunteer to help me demonstrate the tango. *(She pauses, as the students stand in silent dread.)* Henry, you will do fine.

Hank. *(Sarcastic, mumbling)* If you insist, Ms. Delfo.

(Hank and Ms. Delfo begin to dance awkwardly: Ms. Delfo is light on her feet and full of energy, while Hank shuffles and drags his feet lethargically.)

Grade 12, Chapter 23

Dramatic Scene
Revising, Editing, and Proofreading

Possible Response:

Ms. Delfo says, "What is wrong with your feet, Henry?"

Hank replies, "Nothing's wrong with my feet, Ms. Delfo."

Ms. Delfo asks, "Then why are you not following my lead?" *(They have been) Hank and Ms. Delfo are attempting to dance to recorded tango music.* (Ital.) *(smirking, sarcastic)*

Hank answers, "It's a long and woeful story, Ms. Delfo. It begins with my dad, who used to take my ma dancing. When he decamped on my sixth birthday, my dear ma made me promise never to dance. ~~(He smurks, he is sarcastic.)~~

Ms. Delfo responds, "I do not believe you."

Grade 12, Chapter 24

Research Report
Drafting and Elaboration

Possible Response:

Four hundred years ago, anyone who wanted to see a play written by William Shakespeare had to go to the Globe Theater. Many plays, such as *Henry IV*, were performed there. The theater was not square but almost round, and the stage, which had three separate entrances, stuck out into the middle of the floor. There were certain features that made the performances particularly interesting. Trap doors allowed props and actors to rise from the floor, and an elevated area behind the stage was sometimes used as a balcony. Elizabethan audiences enjoyed the effect that these elements produced: the loft, high above the stage, represented heaven, and the trap door, leading to a place down below, appeared to be the path to hell.

Grade 12, Chapter 24
Research Report
Revising, Editing, and Proofreading
Possible Response:

The first theater in england enjoyed by many
enthusiastic playgoers was built in 1576. Before
then, most plays ~~are~~ *were* performed by travelling
theater groups. ~~I don't know what the plays~~
~~were.~~ Set up at one end of an inn yard, *When the theater was built,* the
plays were performed outside on a stage. *that was*
The position of the stage allow*ed* the audience to
surround the stage on three sides. There was
no curtain, which *would* normally mark*s* a boundary
between the stage and the audience.

Chapter 25
Lesson 2, page 120
Possible answers:
1. almanac
2. atlas, encyclopedia
3. vertical file
4. encyclopedia
5. biographical dictionary or encyclopedia
6. encyclopedia *or* biographical dictionary
7. vertical file
8. almanac, encyclopedia *or* biographical
   dictionary

Chapter 26
Lesson 3, page 121
A. *Answers will vary. Possible answers:*
1. The California condor is near extinction.
2. None
3. The Grimké sisters were pacifists and
   abolitionists.
4. None.

B. *Answers will vary. Possible answers:*
1. Shakespeare's writing took many creative
   forms.
2. Several Ivy League colleges are in New
   England.

Lesson 4, page 122
1. Circular reasoning
2. False cause
3. Oversimplification
4. Oversimplification
5. Oversimplification
6. Evading the issue *or* false cause
7. Overgeneralization
8. Overgeneralization
9. Either/or fallacy

Chapter 27
Lesson 6, page 123
A.
1. negative
2. affirmative
3. affirmative
4. negative
5. affirmative

B. *Answers will vary. Possible answers:*
1. studies on how furloughs help to reform
   prisoners and reintegrate them into the
   outside world; specific examples of
   prisoners who have done well on furloughs;
   quotes from wardens who are in favor of
   furloughs
2. statistics of crimes committed by prisoners
   on furlough; quotes from law enforcement
   officials; interviews given to the media by
   families harmed by prisoners on furloughs;
   interviews with politicians about their
   constituents' opposition to furlough
   programs

Lesson 6, page 124
Answers will vary. Possible answers:
1. Sentence 6; insufficient or inaccurate
   evidence
2. Sentence 9; evidence that could lead to a
   different conclusion
3. Sentence 10; biased evidence or evidence
   from an unreliable source
4. Students, administrators, teachers,
   and concerned parents should elect
   representatives to determine the policy best
   suited to protect students' rights against
   both invasion of privacy and the distribution
   of drugs in school.

Chapter 30
Lesson 1, page 125
Answers will vary. Possible answers:
1. common, ordinary
2. a fruit like a plum
3. natural talent or ability
4. having similar tastes and interests
5. affluence, wealth

Lesson 2, page 126
Answers will vary. Possible answers:
1. grati; pleasant, satisfying; gratuity
2. geo; pertaining to force caused by the
   earth's rotation; geography
3. corp; to bring together a singular body; corps
4. micro, bio, log; the branch of biology that
   deals with microorganisms; microscope
5. lumin; giving off light; illuminate
6. anthrop; someone who dislikes people;
   anthropologist

7. sol; the state of being alone; solo
8. bibl, phil; lover of books; bibliography
9. vis; to imagine, to see in one's mind; visible
10. phob; exaggerated, illogical fear; hydrophobia

Lesson 3, page 127
Answers will vary. Possible answers:
1. base word = induct; suffix = ee; one who is inititated or enrolled
2. prefix = circum; base word = navigate; to sail or fly around
3. prefix = pre; base word = suppose; to suppose beforehand
4. prefix = equi; base word = distant; of equal distance
5. prefix = hypo; base word = thesis; underlying theory
6. base word = read; suffix = able; capable of being read
7. prefix = mal; base word = content; dissatisfied, rebellious
8. prefix = super; base word = impose; to put on top of, or above, something else
9. prefix = intra; base word = state; within a state
10. base word = meteor; suffix = ic; pertaining to meteors

Grade 12, Chapter 31
Lesson 1, page 128
A. *Answers will vary. Possible answers:*
1. journalism, law, sports
2. four-year college
3. try for scholarship, apply for student loans

B. Answers will vary. Encourage students to be completely honest. After completing the answers, suggest that they make a list of careers or schools that may be of interest and fit their needs.

Lesson 3, page 129
Answers will vary. Encourage students to be completely honest when writing the essay. The essay should be coherent and follow grammar and usage rules.

Lesson 4, page 130
Answers will vary. Students should demonstrate an understanding of how to complete a résumé.

Lesson 4, page 131
Possible answer:
1. 17 Acheron Drive
   Friendsville, Maryland 21531
   April 14, 2000
2. Personnel Director
   Acme Insurance Co.
   P.O. Box 460
   Rockville, Maryland 20856
3. Dear Sir or Madam:
4. I am applying for the position of general clerk that you advertised. I believe I am very qualified for such a position. Last summer I worked as an office clerk at Smith's Insurance Co. in Friendsville, where my work was greatly appreciated. You may contact Mr. Smith at (410) 555-1212 to find out more about my job performance. I am enclosing my résumé, and I look forward to hearing from you.
5. Yours truly,
6. [student's signature]
   Randall K. Jacobs